LONG-RANGE PLANNING FOR

Urban Research and Development

TECHNOLOGICAL CONSIDERATIONS

A Report by the Committee on Urban Technology
Division of Engineering, National Research Council
National Academy of Sciences
National Academy of Engineering

Published by   National Academy of Sciences   Washington, D.C.   1969

This is a report of work under Contract No. H-829
of June 30, 1967
between the Department of Housing and Urban Development
and the
National Academy of Sciences

Publication 1729

Available from
Printing and Publishing Office
National Academy of Sciences
2101 Constitution Avenue
Washington, D.C.   20418

Library of Congress Catalog Card Number: 77-601567

Preface

This report on the strategies, capabilities, and technological considerations for long-range planning of urban research and development responds to a request from the Department of Housing and Urban Development for advice.

At the organizing meeting, the Committee was made aware that the Department of Housing and Urban Development intended to proceed simultaneously with major efforts in policy evaluation, research, and development; that the Department's efforts were organized in four areas of major concern— land use and community development, housing, public facilities and services, and assistance to local government administration; and that only a part of the federal mission in urban areas rests with the Department. But the Secretary is authorized to call upon other federal agencies to supply information he considers necessary to discharge the Department's responsibilities, including assistance to the President in coordinating metropolitan development efforts of all federal agencies.

The study efforts were to devote attention to the following:

1. To delineate the kinds of research capabilities that the Department of Housing and Urban Development should either strengthen or, if lacking, seek to establish, to ensure that its research dollars would be spent most effectively;

2. To make recommendations not only to bring the many facets of urban problems into focus and to define these problems more sharply, but also to mobilize and augment the widespread capabilities now available for solving these problems, that is, to consider the applicability of a total systems approach;

3. To consider means for attracting and training the required professional manpower;

4. To identify broad alternative and complementary strategies available to encourage industry to develop and put into practice useful new technologies and cost-reducing approaches to the problems of housing and urban affairs;

5. To seek to identify constraints imposed by tradition, present practices, and present federal organization and legislative authorities;

6. To ensure that the behavioral and social science research capabilities of academic institutions are optimally organized and effectively utilized in the long-range research and development activities of the Department of Housing and Urban Development; and

7. To specify the kinds of major social, economic, political, and institutional questions that should be raised and answered in order to establish a reliable basis for long-range research and development plans and programs.

The Committee's deliberations included five meetings of the Committee as a whole following the organizing meeting. In addition, five Committee task forces were formed to concentrate on specific topic areas within the Committee's task. Liaison was maintained with the Committee on Social and Behavioral Urban Research. All these activities were scheduled to meet the request of the Department of Housing and Urban Development for completion of the final report in August 1968.

The report calls attention to technological considerations and operating strategies that will assist the Department of Housing and Urban Development in its research and development program planning, budgeting, and implementation. Specific programs conceived during the Committee's deliberations are mentioned as examples of the types of opportunities that should be sought. Portions of the report reflect concern for the social and behavioral considerations and requirements affecting the application of technology. However, detailed treatment of research and development involving the social and behavioral factors in urban affairs is provided in the report of the Committee on Social and Behavioral Urban Research, *A Strategic Approach to Urban Research and Development—Social and Behavioral Science Considerations.* In publishing its findings, the Committee hopes that they will stimulate others in the universities, in local governments, in foundations, and in industry to contribute as they can to urban development.

J. F. Young, *Chairman*
Committee on Urban Technology

Contents

vii

Introduction

A large proportion of the total population of the United States is concentrated in a relatively small number of metropolitan areas, each containing a population of 500,000 or more. In the view of many observers, the nation is entering an advanced stage of development in which, if their predictions are correct, a relatively small number of large, dispersed urban complexes will soon be the residence of the overwhelming majority of Americans. The simple urban pattern of the past—discrete cities surrounded by open country—is gone. Instead, urban complexes are covering increasingly large geographic areas and are comprising numerous large cities, hundreds of small cities and towns, and thousands of suburbs.

This process of increasing urban expansion is a matter of deep concern. It suggests a continuation of many familiar ills—the ungracefulness of urban sprawl, time-consuming and hazardous travel, excessive cost of public services and their requisite physical plants, economic decay in the inner city, slums, crime, and a befouled physical environment.

The Challenge The growth of urban complexes does not, by itself, require continuation or extension of these characteristics. The challenge is to understand the forces that determine the urban character and to guide them in achieving the ends desired by society.

Cities serve as the intersections for many interrelated subsystems, for example, health systems, educational systems, employment systems, transportation systems, recreational systems, governmental systems, and systems for food, clothing, and housing. The interaction and overlapping involved in the operation of these many subsystems greatly increase the complexity of each city system and the difficulty of studying and understanding it.

1

Relatively little research has been undertaken to gain understanding of these subsystems and the complexity of their interrelationships. Engineering work, too, has not been sufficient to provide a recognized body of technology and criteria for urban design and planning.

The Place of Technology   The Department of Housing and Urban Development requested the Committee on Urban Technology to place emphasis on the development of new technologies and improved cost-reducing approaches that would meet urban needs. While there will be opportunities from time to time to undertake the development of new technology to contribute to the managerial, to the physical, and to the planning aspects of urban development, the greater immediate opportunity is to apply technology that is now available but has not been brought to bear on perceived urban needs.

Technology is the body of knowledge, precepts, concepts, and lore that has been gained through the study of nature and through the experience of applications, especially of those utilizing the scientific attitude and method. Accordingly, technology is developed from the work of research and the work of engineering. The purpose of physical research is to gain understanding of the laws of nature or to establish knowledge of phenomena. Engineering has the goal of applying that understanding and knowledge, along with lore, to the design of components, equipment, and systems that satisfy the material, economic, and social needs of society.

At this stage of the nation's response to urban problems, there appears to be more limitation on the knowledge of the social needs to be fulfilled and on the requirements of our communities than on the availability of technology that can contribute to meaningful solutions. There has not been the companion development of a social technology, the knowledge and lore derived from research and applications concerning the nature of man and his society. There is a need for what might be described as a "social engineer," an individual who applies the understanding and knowledge gained from the social and behavioral sciences. Both physical technology and social technology must be brought together in evaluating and implementing solutions to urban problems.

Accordingly, the development of the social engineer through the efforts of the universities, of municipal governments, and of the Department of Housing and Urban Development should have the highest priority. This type of capability is essential to define the needs and thus provide the performance objectives to be satisfied by evaluation of the wealth of available physical technology. As technological applications proceed, experience should show opportunity for development of new technology specifically oriented toward urban problems that will make a further contribution.

The Aspiration Gap   Observation and study of the civil disturbances that occurred during the summer of 1967 and those that have followed emphasize that participation was not limited to the uneducated and the unemployed who had recently moved to the area. It is understood that most participants were born in the communities involved, had partial or complete high school educations, had above-minimal rental housing, and were employed. So the cause was not a general lack of education and employment. There is reason to believe that many participants were motivated to help others who had less and to express dissatisfaction with the gap between their own present realization and their aspirations. Significantly, few, if any, homeowners were involved in the Detroit riots during the summer of 1967. It would appear that a key requirement is to generate opportunity for urban residents and, in this way, to foster attitudes needed for the development of individual capability, of responsibility, and of reward.

In this context, the efforts already under way in many areas of our society to increase the availability of jobs and low-cost housing for the less-skilled, while essential and helpful, are not sufficient by themselves. Social, behavioral, and motivational considerations deserve equal if not greater attention. In the framework of the community as a whole, attention to these aspects of urban development appears essential to gain the community environment and opportunity that will underlie the positive contributions that urban residents can and ultimately will make to society.

Dimensions of Urban Development Needs It is difficult to put precise dimensions on the resources that will finally be required to accomplish the national aspirations for urban development. But the momentum of urban decay and the rising outbreaks of civil disorder indicate, as the Kerner report has documented, that the resources of all sectors of society must be brought to bear on the problem. The federal, state, and municipal efforts to develop understanding of the problem, to devise an environment for productive application of the efforts of many institutions represented in society, and to give guidance to approaches that can be applied broadly are, of course, essential. These efforts must also develop an environment and means for bringing the incentives of the private sector to bear on the problem.

Not only are the dimensions large, but they are also very complex. The interrelationships of the community system, spanning numerous jurisdictions of government and complex physical and social interacting systems, underline the importance of avoiding a piecemeal attack. The community structure should be viewed as a whole to be sure each program enhances community development rather than treating just a single symptom. There should be a multiplicity of research and development tasks that explore, test, and define community requirements and prove the validity of applications. Proof on a limited scale appears to be an essential step before widespread applications are undertaken in a large number of cities.

Research and development of technology require undertaking new designs. Some can be evaluated on paper; others will require experimental applications. When such applications are implemented, they offer two particular advantages. One is the visible evidence to society, especially the area resident, of an energetic response to urban needs. This appears to be essential to instill hope among all concerned. The second advantage is the opportunity for concurrent and postproject social and behavioral research afforded by the mechanism of such technological applications.

The dimensions of urban needs also suggest that efforts must extend over a substantial period of time. The requirements and aspirations of Americans continue to grow, and there is no simple formula for the improvement of communities, nor can it be done overnight. Calling upon the resources of the entire society will bring a large portion of the population into direct participation. This will facilitate understanding and may enhance the patience that seems essential. It will certainly accelerate achievement of motivational maturity. The Department of Housing and Urban Development will need continuing advice and guidance to keep pace with this changing environment. Mechanisms that give the Department access on a continuing basis to objective resources working in the urban-community environment appear essential.

Report Structure Members of the Committee recognized the foregoing characteristics of the present urban environment and responded to the Department's request with these conditions in mind.

Major conclusions and key recommendations are presented first for the benefit of those who wish to gain an overview of the Committee's effort.

The body of the report is organized in four chapters. The first two chapters review considerations particularly related to the staffing and operation of the research and development effort in the Department of Housing and Urban Development. The latter two chapters cover considerations and research and development program recommendations in categories following the present organization of the Department.

Major Conclusions and
Key Recommendations

The Committee believes that the problems of housing and urban development embody the total issue of how men will live together during future decades of technological revolution, of information explosion, and of social change. The quest for ways in which technology can make contributions to this great issue is pursued in the following chapters, but technology can be considered as only one of the tools that are needed and that must be used in helping to evolve the better society and better cities of tomorrow.

MAJOR CONCLUSIONS

1. The momentum of urban decay and the rising outbreak of civil disorders indicate, as the Kerner report has documented, that the resources of all sectors of society must be brought to bear if national aspirations for urban development are to be accomplished.

2. While there are significant research opportunities that will bring forward new technology that will contribute to urban improvement, the primary opportunity resides in the effective application of available technology to the most urgent urban development problems.

3. The national response to urban improvement currently requires greater knowledge of the social needs to be fulfilled and the specific requirements of our communities. Particular emphasis must be given to efforts by the applied social scientists that will define these needs and requirements and thus guide the technological efforts.

4. Many segments of society are responding in one way or another to the desire for urban improvement. If these efforts are to be effectively guided,

coordinated, and measured, it is essential that national goals be developed and quantified where possible.

KEY RECOMMENDATIONS

In this summary, key recommendations are grouped as those of a general administrative nature, those more specifically pertaining to technology, and those that are essentially socioeconomic.

GENERAL RECOMMENDATIONS

1. The magnitude and importance of the urban problems warrant applying substantially more of the Department's staff to its urban research and development mission. The ability to absorb new personnel, the efficient deployment of assigned resources, and probable growth that can be supported suggest an annual doubling of the research and development effort each year for at least three years.

2. The immediate planning efforts of the Department should be directed toward three major objectives:

a. Program planning. This will require (1) examination of historical trends, (2) establishment of an information system, (3) research and analysis of the urban environment for opportunities and constraints, (4) development of criteria for program evaluation, and (5) synthesis and evaluation of alternative courses of action.

b. Short-term projects. These are projects that can be implemented early and yield contributions in one to three years.

c. Long-range projects. Study efforts that may be expected to yield contributions in a 5- to 10-year period.

3. The Department should develop two types of action plans:

a. A plan for fast, orderly, and selective growth within the present limited-war environment.

b. A contingent plan of increased activities to be undertaken coincident with the conclusion of United States participation in the Vietnam war.

4. A structure for the continuous evaluation of the results of urban-technology programs should be developed; approximately 5 to 10 percent of the program funds should be devoted to evaluation. More may be needed to guide and support program-planning.

5. Initial programs should stress sociological and behavioral study projects to delineate the needs and socioeconomic cost–benefit of proposed programs for urban development. Technological research and development programs should stress the visible efforts and provide, where possible, a vehicle for related sociological research.

6. In order to develop effective programs, the Department should build a logical-decision structure to analyze the urban environment, to identify and define urban problems and the manner in which the determinants to these problems interrelate, and so to evaluate the relative cost and benefit of feasible alternative technological contributions.

7. In addition to the competence required to devise a logical-decision structure for program development, the Department will require engineers possessing a knowledge of the state of the art of technology and of the applicability of specific technology to the solution of urban problems. It will also require individuals capable of specifying the social requirements of each urban problem and the relative benefit that would accrue in solving each problem. In this way, the Department will have the capability of synthesizing feasible alternatives and evaluating the worth of these alternatives.

8. An information service should be established for correlating and disseminating data on urban research and development activities under way at the federal, state, and municipal levels.

9. The Department should develop a staff project-management structure for monitoring, guidance, and correlation of projects developed within the Department but carried out elsewhere under contract.

10. The Department is urged to make provisions for the discretionary use of some portion of contracted funds, to develop mechanisms to process unsolicited proposals and thus gain the benefit of inputs of this kind, and to support state and local research and development programs through contract.

11. The Department should assume the leadership in establishing a mechanism to correlate the mission responsibilities of all the federal agencies concerned with various aspects of urban research and development planning. In addition to representation from the federal agencies, there should be representation of the viewpoints of industry, universities, and special institutions.

12. The Department should provide adequate incentives to encourage expansion of educational opportunities available for the production of the specialists who are needed to conceive and develop the programs essential to urban research and development.

13. The Department should encourage national conferences on urban development and should provide financial sponsorship for them.

14. To develop and maintain a successful program of technological urban research and development during these times of rapid change, it is essential that the Department seek continuing broad advice and guidance through

groups having access to both multidisciplinary and specialized resources capable of viewing objectively the needs of urban development in terms of a systems approach.

TECHNOLOGICAL RECOMMENDATIONS

1. A series of carefully chosen large-scale experiments should be undertaken to explore the significant implications and applications of balanced systems for community improvement.

2. The Department is urged to take the leadership in continued exploration of opportunities for further developments in industrialized housing production.

3. The potential opportunities of the community service center concept for the organization and distribution of discretionary services should be studied and evaluated. An early stage of the research undertaking should seek information about appropriate layouts and combinations of facilities within structures.

4. The feasibility and usefulness of sophisticated systems for nondiscretionary services should be evaluated in full-scale field experiments in several communities and in several variations. Such experiments should work to evaluate the desirability and economics of combined service tunnels for utilities such as water, energy, communication, chilled water for air conditioning, and waste disposal.

5. The promise of improvement of rail-guided and independently controlled vehicles for use in urban areas and of short-haul aircraft technology should be kept in focus as a part of urban transportation planning.

6. In Departmental programs associated with the planning of expensive long-lived public facilities systems, allowance should be made for future application of forecasted technology to avoid obsolescence.

7. Efforts should be made to encourage further development needed for adapting the performance criteria concept as a possible alternative to design-specification-type building codes.

SOCIOECONOMIC RECOMMENDATIONS

1. The task of urban development cannot be undertaken without consideration of and planning for the interrelationship of the whole community, including both the suburbs and the urban areas. The Department is urged to incorporate this viewpoint in the planning and in the implementation of urban development programs.

2. Professional and managerial services of the private sector should be used.

3. Seminars and continuing dialogue with representative industrial leaders

should be conducted to assess the needs of industry in specific inner-city situations to reduce investment risks and encourage participation in community improvement efforts.

4. The concept of coventure participation by subcontractors from minority groups should be fostered.

5. Research for low-cost housing should seek means to reduce all cost elements, especially those outside of construction, and should consider the mixed utilization of new construction, refurbishing, upgrading, and relocation.

6. Support should be provided for research efforts seeking improvements in management techniques and the removal of existing constraints such as those outlined in *Research and Experimental Strategy for Community and Urban Excellence* (RESCUE) (Appendix A).

7. The Department should encourage the drafting of model enabling legislation to assist local governments to modernize local laws and regulations that impede the development and implementation of needed urban programs.

8. An inventory should be taken of the capabilities that now exist or that might be developed in the universities. This should then be compared with a projection of requirements for professional manpower to determine a basis for further fellowship support.

9. Universities should be encouraged to join their efforts with local governments and industry to develop viable programs of education seeking to improve the capability of those involved in urban management.

10. More opportunities should be generated for universities to undertake basic research into the nature of urban life and for applied and developmental research intended to evaluate alternative strategies for change.

11. Consideration should be given to the possibility of a professional city management. How might it be trained? How many persons will be required? How best can such a profession contribute to municipal decision-making? Is there a need for a civil-service type of system to give the profession continuity? How can the education of individuals for this profession be related to evolving university programs, municipal programs, and community laboratory centers?

1

Research and Development Strategies

In formulating strategies for a research and development program in the urban area, it is essential to bear in mind that, in general, more technology is available than is being effectively used. Research and development on technology in federally sponsored programs in areas where cost is less controlling than in the urban area is chiefly responsible for this situation. While research on new technology should be continued, what is needed most are strategies and programs that develop available technology for effective application to the most urgent urban problems. This will require the evaluation of many alternatives and the capability of performing cost–effectiveness studies.

Strategies recommended for adoption by the Department of Housing and Urban Development in the management of its research and development program with respect to planning, funding, program development, evaluation, systems approach, information systems, and proposals are presented.

PLANNING

Various approaches that the Department might use in planning its immediate program were reviewed by the Committee. It recommends that the program include the establishment of goals and efforts of three distinct types: program planning, short-term projects, and long-range projects.

10

Establishment of Goals Because the benefits of a clear and consistent set of goals are essential to effective planning and communication, the establishment of goals for the Departmental mission is of the greatest immediate importance. Insofar as possible, goals should be stated in quantified terms so that progress can be measured.

Program Planning Program planning should be designed to determine what needs to be done and in what sequence. Implementation of a program in support of the established goals will require the development of a comprehensive structure for planning that should include examination of historical trends, establishment of an information system, analysis of the urban environment for opportunities and constraints, development of criteria for program evaluation, and synthesis and evaluation of alternative courses of action.

Short-Term Projects Projects that can be implemented early and yield contributions in one to three years should be visible, recognized as relevant, well selected, and well executed, and they should have the leverage of application in more than one community. Meaningful results from the projects must be disseminated to all potential users in an organized fashion. Early programs should be characterized as studies, developments, or pilot operations to identify with the learning process and the efforts of all concerned with urban problems. This would simplify administrative and jurisdictional requirements at this early stage, since the work envisioned should be completed before extension to other agencies and areas.

Long-Range Projects The objectives of long-range, more comprehensive study efforts that might be expected to yield contributions in a 5- to 10-year period should be to expand resources of information basic to solving urban problems and continuous improvement in mechanisms for coordination among federal, state, and municipal agencies and with the activities of the private sector.

FUNDING

Budgetary Allocations In making budgetary provision to accomplish the foregoing planning program, approximately 10 percent of the funding could be justified for planning of Departmental research; approximately half of the funding—50 to 60 percent—should be put into projects for early implementation. This would leave some 30 to 40 percent for long-range projects. These allocations should be expected to vary from time to time as the Department appraises the timeliness and worth of programs in one category versus another.

Over-All Funding The present level of urban research and development funding represents only a beginning when viewed in the light of the indicated needs of society. Two strategies derive from this condition:

1. *The necessity for selective planning of the current action program to get the greatest meaningful return with the limited funds available.* The efforts selected must demonstrate a sound approach to solving community improvement problems, if further support is to be obtained from the public and the Congress in balance with other demands on the national economy.

2. *The optimal rate of growth.* The need suggests that the Department's activity should grow as fast as possible, at least in the early years. Absorption of new personnel, efficient development of assigned resources, and the probable rate that could be supported suggests that an optimal rate for the Department's growth would be an annual doubling of its funds for research and development over the next 3 to 5 years.

Capability should be evaluated periodically to establish optimal levels of resources that can be applied to cope with the needs for urban improvement.

Planning for growth is necessarily a two-step process. First, there must be a buildup of capability—specifically, an increase in the number of competent persons qualified to do the necessary program planning and development; second, as this capability is achieved, the rate of funding for implementation should be increased.

While this increased rate of activity might initially appear to be greater than those not close to the problem might have anticipated, only a large, well-managed, ultimately broadscale program can attract the competence needed by the Department to perform its role and to stimulate local governments and the private sector to devote more manpower and financial resources to the over-all program. An effort of this magnitude, conducted within the framework of a well-understood set of goals and missions, should achieve the results necessary to assure the public and the Congress that the problems are being competently addressed.

Accordingly, it is urgent that the Department develop two types of action plans:

1. *A plan for fast, orderly, and selective growth within the present limited-war environment.* If the Vietnam war continues at its present pace, a rate of growth that would double the Department's research and development effort each year for 3 to 5 years should be taken as an initial step.

2. *A contingent plan of accelerated activities to be undertaken coincident with the conclusion of United States participation in the Vietnam war.* This

plan would depend on the capability that has been achieved at the time the accelerated allocation of resources would be made available, and could involve enhancement of research, of development, or of application efforts.

PROGRAM DEVELOPMENT

With the existing limited funding, action programs must be highly selective and must demonstrate a sound approach to solving community improvement problems if they are to generate further support by the public and the Congress.

Design of low-cost housing; of transportation systems; of utilities; of governmental, educational, and health facilities; and the incorporation of the amenities essential to a positive community attitude are not fundamentally limited by available materials and technologies. Rather, successful design centers on the knowledge of sociological and behavioral requirements and the assessment of the relative worth of various alternatives when considered in the context of the needs of a particular community. Successful implementation depends on good management.

These considerations suggest that, at least initially, Departmental program development and budgeting activities should favor sociological and behavioral projects that identify needs and delineate the requirements for proposed solutions to various problems and the cost–benefit, both social and economic. However, the program should include and maintain a level of technological research and development sufficient to promote viability and visibility in the application of technology, to implement experimental programs having combined sociological and technological character, and to provide a base for further technological program development as sociological requirements are identified.

In programming research and development, it is essential to identify and include those projects that will result in new knowledge and experience that can be used in many municipalities to help make municipal administration more effective, to provide better plans, and to encourage participation of state and local governments, universities, and industries.

Early efforts should be directed toward improving management techniques that will assist in developing cost-reducing approaches to planning and implementing urban improvements that are compatible with social needs.

The relative worth of the available technological alternatives should be examined in seeking the most desirable technological improvements. A review of technological alternatives would be helpful in establishing program priorities in terms of the most feasible combinations of applied technology to achieve sought-after social and economic values. Long-range research and development programs might well include projects seeking major technological breakthroughs as part of their objectives.

EVALUATION

A structure for continuous evaluation of the results of the application of technology to the spectrum of community problems is as important as good program planning, budgeting, and program development.

Probably not less than 5 percent and as much as 10 percent of the effort expended in the three categories of applied effort recommended in "Planning" should be devoted to evaluation. The development of criteria for evaluation and the scheduling of periodic evaluations should be required elements in all project work statements. Such an approach should ensure maximum learning from each project; identify technology, plans, and programs that deserve dissemination; avoid repetition of less fruitful paths; guide formulation of new projects; and provide experience information to assist in the selection among both solicited and unsolicited project proposals.

SYSTEMS APPROACH

The Committee recommends that the Department view urban development as a total systems problem. A systems approach to defining problems and evaluating plans and programs should include all the elements that impinge on the people, institutions, and facilities of a community. A metropolitan community comprises perhaps the most comprehensive and complex interrelated system aside from the life system of man himself. The social, legal, fiscal, and managerial systems interact with such physical systems as housing, transportation, communication, utilities, waste handling, business, and industry.

Relatively little work has been undertaken to define in detail either the social or physical nature of this system and its interrelationships. Because of the complexity of the total system, greater progress might be realized by modeling the metropolitan system at the subsystem level. Several points of view might be helpful. For example, the physical system might be separated from the motivational; both might be tested on an added value scale, on geographic and demographic relationships, and in a matrix of function versus facilities. Difficult as such analysis might be, it appears essential that the Department undertake development of a systems framework as part of its planning effort. Such a structure is needed to appraise the cost and value of alternative approaches in solving a given problem. It is also needed as a structure for correlating the program with other agencies, for closing gaps, and for ensuring a comprehensive approach.

One initial approach to developing a total systems framework is the activity of the National Research Council's Building Research Advisory Board (BRAB), which has developed a self-stimulating investigative methodology, as follows: definition of needs and desires, definition of constraints, creative program formulation, demonstrations, and feedback. The method is exemplified in *Research and Experimental Strategy for Community and Urban Excellence* (RESCUE), a report completed by a standing committee of the Building Research Advisory Board in April 1967 (Appendix A). As explained in the BRAB report, a dynamic (iterative) approach is more rewarding than a sequential approach to the solution of urban problems.

INFORMATION SYSTEMS

A fundamental requirement for effective planning and decision-making at all levels, national, state, and local, is information that is both valid and relevant. To meet this requirement, more research and development must be carried out in the whole domain of urban information services, seeking in particular to determine the basis of input information needed for effective management of urban affairs.

Specifically, more significant social indicators must be constructed to measure the consequences of changes. For example, the single act of upgrading workers from a low-skill category to a high-skill category may only serve to stimulate migration of a desirable group of citizens from the city core to the suburbs, with the core remaining the same or getting worse. The single act of replacing a slum with low-cost housing may merely generate a slum elsewhere as a mobile population under uncontrolled social and economic forces readjusts to the situation. One necessity is that suitable and convenient means exist for people in a region to make a living. Even the development of industry within the core is a complex problem because the skills demanded must match the talents within the region. In developing indicators that measure the consequences of change, safeguards should, of course, be employed to protect individual privacy and proprietary information.

Much research is needed to develop adequate models of a city in order to investigate these matters. Considering the wide diversity and character of each city, it is probable that no single model is widely applicable. However, modern computer and information-processing technology could be brought to bear on some of these problems.

An important issue is finding ways to establish urban information systems where the overriding concern is to ensure that the correct logic is built into the system so that answers will be optimum for management decisions.

There are serious problems of implementation. For example, often there is insufficient financial support to permit the initiation of a major attack on the urban-information problem. The cities are not always certain what they should have. And the development of systems that will simultaneously serve many agencies within one city is difficult. While the informational needs of communities will differ, it is believed that the logic for such systems and much of the software programming can be applicable to many municipalities. This would appear to be an important development area for the Department to examine.

PROPOSALS

The range and complexity of the research that must be undertaken is so great that all available resources will need to be individually and jointly involved. Although it is assumed that the newly created Urban Institute will play a central role in this program, the universities and private industry have much to contribute. Private industry should be specially concerned with management and technological development. The full utilization of the research potential of the nation should consider use of a variety of administrative and financial arrangements.

Directed Contracts   The present system of requests for proposals should be extended. As long as the Department of Housing and Urban Development does not contain an in-house research capability, the specific projects that are developed within the Department will have to be carried out elsewhere and will have to be monitored, guided, and correlated through a project management structure to be developed within the Department. The National Aeronautics and Space Administration policy of "selecting out" 10 to 20 percent of the project managers each year as an upgrading process and stimulant to develop competence in a new and undefined field should be considered as a policy-objective of the Department.

Many projects should be carried by private research agencies and the private entrepreneurial community with experience in practical matters of urban development. Some will be appropriate for urban institutes and the universities, however, and invitations to respond to such proposals should continue to go to those institutions having specific capabilities in the relevant areas of technology and applied science and having unique opportunity to work with local governments.

Discretionary Funding   In its research contracts the Department should provide for discretionary use of some portion of the research funds available.

Discretionary funding brings forth new ideas, sometimes of more significance than the original project. It is believed that the Department would benefit by providing an increased level of discretionary funding for those having a record of prudent and creative use of such project flexibility. A range of just a few percentage points of project funding for early endeavors to as high as 15 percent for the more experienced researchers and mature projects appears appropriate.

Unsolicited Research Proposals The Department should make sums available to support unsolicited research proposed by industry, by universities and other institutions, and by individual scholars. On the assumption that it is desirable to encourage promising research input wherever it can be found, a program of grants should be established to support such research projects. Such a program would require staff competence to evaluate the relevancy of the proposals received, to discriminate among the applicable alternatives, and to establish priorities for implementation. Arrangements to fulfill this function should be made, however, in order to ensure that the Department will have the full benefit of participation by those capable of contributing original thinking to the solution of urban problems. Projects financed under this program would serve to feed new ideas into the more mission-oriented Urban Institute.

2

Research and Development Resources and Capabilities

In a problem as pressing as the crisis of our cities it is natural that virtually all responsible citizens and institutions should seek ways in which they can make a contribution. This is already true of most of the federal agencies in one way or another. There is increasing activity on the part of universities and considerable activity among industrial leaders working with heads of local government. Programs to meet urban research needs are forming within existing nonprofit institutions, and new institutions designed to concentrate in the urban field are being established. In aggregate these possess a potential wealth of contribution, but they also represent a burgeoning group of independent, sometimes duplicative, resources that must be coordinated if society is to realize their full potential.

Considerable experimentation is warranted in evolving ways for universities, special institutions, industries, local research and development groups, and other federal agencies to participate effectively in the urban program.

UNIVERSITIES

The traditional functions of the university have been teaching, research, and public service. While the universities have increasingly adapted to interdisciplinary opportunities, many are presently not structured to respond to the urban challenge. And yet the requirements of the times are so great that extraordinary steps must be taken to encourage universities to strengthen and redirect their capabilities and to apply their talents to the vital urban issues of training, of research, and of community participation.

University Education It is apparent that the urban problem cannot be assigned to any one of the traditional disciplines of the university. What was originally thought to be primarily a technological problem of rebuilding and replacing the community plant has now obviously become a complex social problem of finding ways in which enormous conglomerates of people separated by race, class, geography, and political jurisdictions can live together harmoniously and productively. Thus the need for teaching special skills to meet professional needs in urban affairs can be said to be virtually panuniversity. Specialists from such interrelated fields as architecture, city planning, education, engineering, law, public administration, and the social and behavioral sciences will obviously be needed and in ever-increasing numbers. Social engineers with multidisciplinary backgrounds, bearing the same relationship to social scientists as engineers bear to physical scientists, are urgently needed.

The training of professional specialists implies postgraduate study. In order to build such programs with a special urban orientation in the relevant fields, it will be necessary to increase greatly the funds now available. It will no doubt be necessary to expand the curriculum, but this will have little effect unless students are attracted into these specialized areas. The Department should undertake an inventory of the capabilities that now exist and are being developed and compare this with a projection of requirements for professional manpower. Substantial increases in the present fellowship program, both predoctoral and postdoctoral, will undoubtedly be indicated. The present appropriation supports approximately 60 fellowships in urban studies. An increase many times this number is needed.

There is an insufficient supply of professional contributors and teachers, and it is essential that the university capability be maintained to ensure the development of trained personnel for work in the field of urban affairs. This suggests not only the need to avoid recruiting indiscriminately among university staff, but also the necessity to balance research grants between the new Urban Institute and universities so as to attract both professors and students to the field.

One of the quickest ways to fill the gap between the need for and the supply of professional manpower is to embark on a program of mid-career updating of selected people who have a potential for carrying greater responsibility and who are now employed in urban management. This might take the form of a 3-month study of modern urban science and technology (MUST) with lecturers from universities, government, urban institutes, and industry. The idea would be to give a comprehensive picture of the state of the art for urban management concepts and applications as well as a good understanding of the latest developments in applicable technologies. The course should not attempt to make each manager an expert in a narrow discipline, but rather should attempt to orient each toward an increased understanding of relationships, of interfaces, and of the application of modern tools for managing urban affairs.

The training of agricultural professionals in the land-grant colleges has been heavily supported by federal funds and it is equally reasonable that the training of urban professionals should be supported in the same way. It would be desirable to set up programs in universities associated with each of the major metropolitan areas with annual financing large enough (perhaps several hundred thousand dollars) to be effective.

It is believed that this is preferable to the suggestion that new institutions or colleges be established under the title "urban college." The example used as a prototype for this suggestion is the land-grant college. But the analogy is only partially appropriate. The urban problem embraces substantially all the disciplines of modern knowledge. Any move to establish an urban college seems just an alternative way of mobilizing the elements of the modern university, including the engineering college, in new directions and giving it a new sense of purpose.

Many universities now have departments of city government or centers of urban studies and the like, but careful examination usually shows that some of the essential disciplines are not always included or fully involved. Engineering schools, as one example, must play a larger role in these matters in the future.

In many instances, attempts have been made to establish a curriculum for education in urban government. Most have been sterile unless the faculty was itself participating in contemporary urban problems and unless the faculty and the students were active in research on authentic problems. One issue is laboratories where students and professors would test hypotheses by experiments. As a rule, laboratories are established within the confines of the university, but in the urban domain the only authentic laboratory is the city itself.

University Research   There is a great need both for basic research on the nature of urban life and for applied and developmental research intended to evaluate alternative strategies for change. This is true with regard to the technological problems of the cities and it is even more obviously true of their social, economic, and political problems.

In general, the possible role of the universities in seeking solutions to the cities' problems has been greatly underestimated. Admittedly, the mood of the traditional university is not conducive to efficient dialogue between the educational establishment and the city governments. But this need not be so. Civil engineers naturally respond to city problems, and now there is awakened interest in all branches of engineering, from aeronautical regarding airports, to electrical on information technology, to mechanical or chemical on waste disposal and utilities.

A plan for the future would oblige the university to accept responsibility for helping the city and its citizens. Problems of concern to the city should be taken into the institution in ways that would establish a multidisciplinary effort in projects having a clearly defined mission. The traditional scholarly study of the urban problem should more and more give away to the search for an answer to the city's problem.

As President Howard Johnson of M.I.T. said in his inaugural address in October 1966, "The demands upon the university of today to meet the problems of the new world alter the ways in which it performs to fill its basic function."

To seek these altered ways it needs guidelines, and one useful way is to have more of its professors practice in the urban situation either as consultants or advisers to city governments. Traditionally, professors—and especially professors in science and engineering—do this in industry and commerce. If they can do it more and more in city government, they will bring back to the campus more meaningful examples of the problems of the city to enrich the dialogue that is carried on in the classroom.

Mission-Oriented University Urban Institutes Within those universities that have broad capabilities, it is important to move toward the development of new administrative inventions specifically devised to organize cross-disciplinary, mission-oriented research programs. While most universities have little experience with large-scale, program-oriented activities of this type, relevant prototypes have been successfully developed on some campuses. Urban institutes are now being organized in a number of universities, especially in those with a metropolitan location. In general they lack funding and hence are not able to organize the broad interdisciplinary programs that the urban problem requires. The Department should undertake to provide support to make possible the establishment of some full-scale university urban institutes where experience and resources make the investment most promising. These institutes should be designed to be free of the usual disciplinary jurisdictions of the university. With industry's help, they should be staffed with people with a sense of urgency for the urban problem. They should reflect the particular strengths of the campuses on which they are located, integrating both technological and scientific resources and coupling with local governments in all cases.

University Service to the Communities The universities, especially those that are primarily supported by public funds, provide many services to their state and local communities. These are commonly in response to individual requests and do not have the continuity provided to the agricultural community by the land-grant colleges. In order to engage the universities effectively in the process, it would be necessary to organize agencies within them specifically oriented to this function. The mission of these agencies would be to bring the resources of the universities into a productive relationship with the cities, providing training, consultation, technical assistance, and such other applications of university talent as may prove useful. This new type of agency has been described as "a program that is fully engaged with the city, well coordinated within its own university, and flexible enough to incorporate a variety of problem-solving approaches and structural arrangements."

THE URBAN INSTITUTE

The establishment of the Urban Institute introduces two significant relationships with the Department of Housing and Urban Development. One is the opportunity for contributing to the Departmental program under Departmental funding. The other is the potential overlap in programs related to the individual cities.

Support The prospectus issued on April 26, 1968, indicated the intent to bring together in the Institute the many disciplines necessary to an over-all study of urban problems. This would indicate a capability to make a very significant contribution to the Department in fulfilling its planning needs. It could be a source of creative contributions; it could test hypotheses; it could evaluate alternatives; and it could compare evaluations made by other groups. It is recommended that the Department's funding of the new Institute emphasize this kind of contribution to the Departmental mission.

It is recognized that the Department must maintain a top-level competence in this same area and utilize resources available from other contractors such as other nonprofit institutions, universities, and industry.

It is further recognized that the Department's dependence on the Institute will require some continuity of funding at levels sufficient to maintain a healthy, productive, and efficient work force in the Institute devoted to the Department's requirements. This is often referred to as a staff of "critical size." Without appropriate size and continuity, sporadic efforts to develop funding among a multiplicity of sources could detract measurably from the effectiveness of the Urban Institute.

Scope The prospectus also indicated that the Institute would work with individual cities studying their particular problems, developing strategies for action, and providing advice and technical assistance in carrying out such strategies. The dimensions of the urban-development task make it desirable, of course, to utilize the very high-level and specialized capability that the

Institute is expected to develop. The interplay of Institute knowledge and understanding with the knowledge and understanding developed by others should be wholesome. On the other hand, it would appear possible that the efforts of the Institute might in time tend to duplicate those of the Departmental mission and thus limit the effectiveness of the Department.

The Department should explore this with the Administration and seek clarifying procedures that will make the efforts of both organizations most effective.

INDUSTRY

In general, industry represents a major source of professional talent and managerial experience, and it has a basic interest in successful community development. Although a primary capability offered by industry is to undertake design and construction projects, its experience in planning, organization, and general management practices can be a useful source of assistance to local government administration. Industry should be called upon as a source of professional talent in the areas of business administration and technical management to work individually and jointly with local municipal administrations, with universities, and with other institutions for guidance in planning and implementing community development.

Private industry can make a major contribution in developing employment opportunities, in upgrading the inner-city work force to realize greater material gain, and in applying technology to the systems framework and the physical facilities of the inner-city area. Those in industry concerned with project management, and with implementing the worthwhile ideas emanating from research, recognize, however, that achieving this type of contribution will require the development of an appropriate climate for investment. Most industrial leaders need no incentive to try to make a contribution in an area so closely related to national, social, and economic progress. On the other hand, they are not in a position to risk the equity entrusted by their share-owners without at least reasonable protection and return. The encouragement of industrial participation requires the determination of incentives not unlike those provided for industrial participation in underdeveloped countries.

The Department is urged to establish a seminar and continuing dialogue with industry leaders to explore in depth the terms and conditions industry would need in specific community situations to reduce the risks of participation to acceptable levels. This is necessary because, in general, two main factors will govern industrial participation: the risk and the market, that is, the potential volume of activity. One way of overcoming the risk factor is to have private enterprise act as an agent for a government agency. Such an arrangement enables private industry to contribute its management experience and technical capability with minimum risk to the stockholder.

Coventure Subcontracting   It is most important that new ways be found to bring labor minority-group subcontractors and the entrepreneur together in the mainstream of construction. This would be helpful in two principal areas related to urban affairs. First, if minority-group subcontractors can participate as a related part of the entrepreneur structure there should be greater satisfaction of the demands for equal opportunity for employment and, second, it should help develop managerial talent and manpower necessary to meet the extensive construction requirements projected for community development. The Department should explore the implications and possible benefits that might result through coventure participation by minority-group subcontractors and, if warranted, it should develop information on mechanisms for coventure efforts between principal contractors and minority-group subcontractors.

LOCAL DEVELOPMENT CENTERS AND OTHER STUDY GROUPS

In addition to developing national programs designed to have a catalytic effect, the Department of Housing and Urban Development should take steps to broaden the viewpoint and upgrade the professional competence in state and city operating organizations. To initiate this process, numerous small grants should be made to such organizations for the express purpose of placing bright young well-trained "urban professionals" in such operating entities as assistants to the responsible personnel. This experience will serve as an internship for the recent graduates and will also give them a chance to prove their usefulness to the operating staff. A form of grant, in part to the university and in part to the municipality, might serve to attract faculty and graduate students who could, over a period of a year, enhance local university–municipality cooperation.

As experience accumulates, these interns should become especially helpful in carrying out studies that have a broader and longer-range viewpoint than those carried out by people concerned with the day-to-day problems. They should be able to interact well with their counterparts in the universities and industry. As the scope of such studies increases, larger funds should be made available on a contract basis to the state and local groups so that work of this kind can be greatly expanded. However, care should be taken to ensure that funds for such longer-range studies are not diverted into meeting local short-term financial crises.

Clearly not all the small study groups started by such a mechanism will be really productive. In any research operation the ratio of failures to successes may necessarily be high. However, some of the groups should show real promise, and these should be given the opportunity to carry out large-scale experiments of the municipal development center (MDC) type with major long-term funding.

In general, research and development projects at the local level should be encouraged by the Department of Housing and Urban Development to grow as rapidly as competent persons become available to do the work. In fostering local capabilities, the Departmental policy should be one of initial generosity in funding projects deemed to be worthwhile, followed by a critical review and appraisal of accomplishments. Whereas the emphasis in the national research and development program should be strategic, long range, correlative, and designed to fill gaps, the research and development efforts at the local level should be short range and tailored to immediate local needs and the local environment. The local efforts, however, should have the benefit of strategic inputs from the national level, and features of local studies supported by federal funds should have applicability to other municipalities in the nation.

MARSHALING RESEARCH AND DEVELOPMENT RESOURCES AND CAPABILITIES

The major resources and their capabilities for research and development in the urban area have been discussed in the preceding sections. The essential element in bringing them into focus is the level of competence within the Department of Housing and Urban Development. Factors to be considered in enhancing the staff capabilities of the Department and measures that might be taken with a view toward marshaling resources and capabilities are suggested in this section.

Increased Staff Capabilities of the Department The magnitude and importance of the urban problem and the expanding nature of the task ahead warrant a substantial increase in the Department's capabilities as qualified personnel become available. In addition to personnel with a high level of competence in the sociological area, the Department will require persons who are competent in the development and operation of a logical systems analysis structure and persons who are knowledgeable in both the availability and the application of technology in synthesizing feasible alternative solutions to urban problems as well as evaluating the worth of alternative solutions.

Establishment of a Federal Agency Correlating Group   To correlate the mission responsibilities and capabilities of all the federal agencies concerned with various aspects of urban planning, there is a need for representatives from these agencies to meet frequently to evaluate goals. If necessary, the Department should seek authority from the President to establish such a correlating group. The viewpoints of industry, of universities, and of special institutions should be represented, but care should be taken that the group does not become too large and unwieldy.

Establishment of an Information Service   There is a definite need for an information service to correlate research and development activities at all levels responding to urban affairs problems. The elements for such a service must include more than mechanical data processing. An important feature of the service should provide for personal contact and direct correlation of information resulting from urban research and development activities. There should be a number of well-informed persons who make visits to responsive projects that are a part of federal and local programs. The Highway Research Information Service of the National Research Council's Highway Research Board is an example of an effective research correlation and information service.

Expansion of Educational Opportunities   The Department should provide adequate incentives to encourage expansion of educational opportunities available for the development of the specialists who are needed to conceive and implement the programs essential to urban research and development.

Conferences on Urban Affairs   The Department should encourage and provide financial sponsorship for national conferences on urban affairs. Such conferences would provide democratic participation in proposing solutions for national problems, an interchange of ideas, and records of proceedings for reference and study.

3

Technology in the Urban Environment

Emphasizing technological considerations, this report has thus far addressed itself to the following elements of the tasks outlined in the Preface:

1. The broad strategies available to encourage industry to develop and put into practice useful new technologies and cost-reducing approaches;
2. The kinds of research capabilities that the Department should either strengthen or, if lacking, seek to establish;
3. The need for employing a total systems approach in relating the many facets of the urban problem and for mobilizing and augmenting the available resources and capabilities that might contribute to their solution; and
4. The means of attracting and training the required professional manpower.

The nature of the forces involved in urban expansion and the collective experience of Committee members competent in matters of engineering, technology, economics, and the social sciences lead to three basic conclusions by the Committee:

1. In general, more technology is available than is being effectively used. While research in new technology should continue, what is needed most are strategies and programs for utilizing available technology in effective applications to the urban area.
2. The design of systems for community improvement is not fundamentally limited by available materials and technologies; rather it centers on the knowledge of sociological and behavioral requirements and the assessment of the relative value and desirability of various alternatives.

27

3. Identification and selection of useful available technologies for application in a national program for urban development will require a high degree of technical competence in the Departmental staff.

In evaluating the applicability of available technology to the solution of particular problems in the urban environment, it will be found in some instances that while a physically feasible solution would result, it would be economically unacceptable. There will, however, be opportunities for cost reduction through application of technology to city systems. Experience also indicates that a rewarding field in which to seek cost reduction lies in the identification and reduction of constraints imposed by tradition and present practice.

The remainder of this report focuses attention on constraint factors and technological considerations related to local government administration and coordination, land use and community development, housing, and public facilities and services.

LOCAL GOVERNMENT ADMINISTRATION AND COORDINATION

The achievement of efficient management of the modern metropolitan area is one of the most urgent problems facing mankind. As cities become more complex, the citizens' demands for services increase as do their expectations for better standards of living.

The most crucial problems involve inner-city decay, social unrest, and economic instability. As city managers attempt to improve conditions, they find themselves constrained by the effect of improper solutions to past problems. There are many other constraints. City governments are often inadequately staffed in both numbers and kinds of skills required, and the data on which management must base decisions are often inadequate, contradictory, or nonexistent. Further, those engaged in city management invariably find that they must work within a complex framework of agencies whose areas of authority and spheres of jurisdiction overlap and frequently cancel each other.

Not all the doctrines evolved for the management of a business serve as good analogues for the management of a city. The profit motive that so often spurs business management to vigorous action is absent in city management. In industry, both the product and the customer are clearly defined. The city, in contrast, provides the citizens with a complex mixture of services; doctrines that influence the attitude of the citizens provide a rather vague value system. Each element of the city system is highly interactive. While an accurate comprehensive mathematical model of the city system could be of considerable benefit in evaluating the worth of alternative actions, the system is so complex that it is difficult to establish the manner in which interdependent parameters relate.

This complexity of the city management problem is in sharp contrast to the tenure, the preparation, and often the personal objectives of city administrations. This suggests the need for a profession of city management to provide more thorough preparation and greater continuity—a profession that would attract competent people to career positions.

Appraisal Several issues emerge from an analysis of the foregoing situation:

1. There must be a reappraisal of how people are educated for career positions in city government. Concurrent with this issue is the need for procedures to continue to update the competence of management as our understanding of the problem advances and as the complexity of the urban environment increases.

2. There must be a marked increase in the number of trained, able people who will enter city management.

3. There must be a comprehensive reassessment of the decision-making function in government so that it incorporates political, economic, social, and technological issues with appropriate balance.

4. It may be advantageous to make civil service and pension rights transferable between jurisdictions.

From this it follows that a more structured, relevant base of information must be provided, as well as improved indications of the change of urban forces, in order to improve the quality of administrative decision-making. This leads to the need for improved data-gathering and information-processing systems for city management.

Professional Education The approach to maintaining an adequate supply and a desired level of competence of personnel in career positions in city government was discussed in Chapter 2. Opportunities to work with academic institutions and industry should be welcomed by city administrators. One way of relating to university capability might be to create openings for young faculty members or for graduate students to spend a year or more as city employees, with freedom to maintain close and formal relations with the urban research facilities of their home institutions. Such a cooperative urban fellowship program could become a means for recruiting and developing social engineers.

Career Incentives Individuals who prepare themselves for undertaking work in urban development will in the course of their careers be required to move from one assignment to another, in some instances at relatively frequent intervals. This suggests that a civil service system covering career employment in urban affairs should be developed to provide equitable compensation and appropriate benefits to individuals as they move through various assignments and responsibilities within and between jurisdictions.

Municipal Development Planning The effective application of technology in urban design is important in providing flexibility in city patterns. Because there is a deep need on the part of individuals to have some control over their environment and to participate in actions that influence their destiny, the development of urban designs must involve the participation of people at the neighborhood level in decisions that intimately affect them. In general, satisfaction and cooperation can be obtained only when individuals are involved early enough to understand the difficulties and compromises that are inevitably involved.

Long-range planning is an important ingredient in urban development regardless of the size or complexity of the urban area. One reason for this is the overlapping among the several systems involved in urban development. City administrators can borrow to considerable advantage from the techniques used by large corporations. Typically, the aim of corporate planning is to establish goals that are reasonably attainable and action plans that are sufficiently flexible to permit the achievement of the goals. To retain their full effectiveness, urban goals must be reviewed periodically for possible changes that could increase their relevance, and the implementation of urban action plans must be characterized by flexibility in the managerial processes. As in the corporate structure, where competition requires an alert management, the city administrator must be alert to the changing scene and the need for innovations in the organizational structure to enhance the capability to perform.

A major complicating factor facing the city administrator in planning for possible solutions and in implementing them is that city revenues are falling far behind the need for reasonable expenditures in support of community improvement. As long-range plans are developed, it will often become apparent that that their implementation will require modernization of existing laws and regulations. To assist the states and municipalities, the Department of Housing and Urban Development should develop the capability for drafting model legislation for information and guidance.

LAND USE AND COMMUNITY DEVELOPMENT

The building of circumferential and access freeways designed around present technology means that greater distances can be traversed per hour and that the area accessible on a time basis from a given point increases rapidly with increases in vehicle speed and extension of the road network. This means that people, industry, and commerce now have the opportunity to enjoy more space.

Adequate land is available for the foreseeable expansion of urban areas. Urbanized land areas now encompass roughly 40,000 square miles (about 1.3 percent of the total contiguous land area, exclusive of primary water bodies, of more than 2,950,000 square miles). By 1980, although the total urban area may be about 77,500 square miles, still the total urbanized area is expected to be under 3 percent of the gross land area. Cities are spreading; however, in their spreading they are absorbing an extremely small percentage of the land. Moreover, cities are absorbing land at a slower rate than agricultural land is becoming surplus. In large measure, the reason for this differential is that agricultural productivity is increasing at a greater rate than the population is increasing. While the spreading of urban areas has negligible impact on the national agricultural picture, such continual spreading is engendering certain urban problems—problems associated with changing sociological, economic, and technological patterns.

Migration to the Suburbs Migration to the suburbs caused the population per square mile in metropolitan areas to drop from 411 persons per square mile in 1950 to 365 persons per square mile in 1960. The density is now approaching 355; as roads and other transport facilities improve, the area officially recognized to be functioning as part of metropolitan communities is growing faster than the population. In the more densely settled portions of the cities, in what the Census calls urbanized areas, there were 5,400 persons per square mile, or just under 8.5 per acre, in 1950. The density dropped to less than 6 persons per acre in 1960 and now may be down to less than 5 percent per acre.

A major problem in cities, whether they are growing or relatively stable in population, is the shift of many people in the upper-level income groups away from the center. The nature of this population shift may be due in large part to a more rapid increase in desirable living facilities and also in professional and technical employment opportunities in suburbia as compared with the rate of increase of acceptable jobs in the central city.

Families at and above the middle-income level moving to the suburbs, together with the increased development of industry and commerce in the suburbs, tend to make the rise in tax revenue for the center of the city lag behind the rate of growth of tax income in the suburbs. Although some of the higher-value commercial activity tends to stay in the city, the city is usually left with a tax income that is low in relation to needs. Changing conditions suggest the need for continuous reappraisal of the nature of the requirements for public services and facilities in the central city. Opportunities for improved organization and administration of facilities and services with attendant economies need to be identified. Adding to the imbalance is the migration of surplus farm labor to the cities, increasing the cities' burdens for welfare and other services. In most instances, these services cannot be supported entirely from existing levels of local revenue.

Studies are needed to explore opportunities to encourage local communities to use their full revenue capabilities and minimize the need for assistance from nonlocal sources of public revenue. As a counterpart of these studies, criteria might be developed for determining when federal or state subsidy is justified or for determining the feasibility of obtaining payment from one community for services rendered by another. It would be helpful to local governments if there were national criteria for optimum taxing and borrowing before federal or state subsidy is justified.

The Need for Free Flow within Metropolitan Areas   One cause of urban unrest is that, in general, the amenities of the suburbs are not available to certain minority groups. Although many minority peoples prefer to remain with their own ethnic group in the city, rebuilding decayed areas to provide improved housing is an incomplete solution to their aspirations. Those who desire to move outside the central city often find it impossible to obtain accommodations compatible with their economic status.

On the other hand, in the suburbs there are many mature couples whose children are grown, and who might prefer the convenience of living in the city if it were safe and attractive. Their participation in city affairs and their contribution, directly and indirectly, to city revenues could be of benefit to the city.

Downtown centers developed during the 19th century are characterized by high density and concentration. Present technological capabilities for improved transportation and communication facilities make lower density possible, higher incomes make it feasible, and public preference seems to suggest that it is desirable. People presently immobilized in the central city should have the opportunity to communicate or merge with the rest of the population in a low-density environment if it is within their means and desires to do so. Attention should be given to the lack of free flow within the central city and within the suburbs, and between these areas. In this context the task of urban development cannot—and should not—be undertaken without consideration and planning of the interrelationship of the total community, including both the suburbs and the urban areas.

Land Value for Low-Income Housing   Today's land values in central city areas are affected by the potential returns from high-value commercial, professional, financial, and multifamily residential activities; illegal use in some instances; community services; and anticipation that values in central areas will be protected by the federal government or by inflation. If land with a potential high value for nonresidential use must be used temporarily for low-income housing, it would appear to be advantageous to design renewal housing for a short life. If land values are high as a result of illegal use in which buildings and their occupancy are not in compliance with existing codes, the problem is more difficult. If satisfactory housing could be built or existing structures rehabilitated in sufficient quantity and could be made available at rents or purchase prices low enough to create sufficient vacancies, then codes could be enforced. A sizable vacancy figure would give the flexibility needed for code enforcement, and property values should then drop to supportable levels.

Access to Jobs It is often difficult for core-city residents to find jobs, not only because their skills are inadequate for today's requirements, but also because jobs are not always available in readily accessible locations. The most immediately obvious solution, disregarding the social consequences, would be either to move the residents closer to the jobs or to provide better access from the central city to the jobs.

Adequate freeways to the centers of cities could provide better access, but a major obstacle has been the displacement of those living along the proposed routes. This obstacle might be reduced if a concept were developed in which highway departments could accept responsibility for providing new facilities, both community and cultural, for persons displaced. For example, if 50 families were moved, they would be resettled en masse, with appropriate amenities. Simply paying the estimated market value of the houses demolished is insufficient; the value of the community to its inhabitants is greater than the sum of the value of the houses, or even the total physical properties. Measures designed to replace total value deserve consideration.

Another approach that will be fruitful in some combinations of metropolitan density, job and residential location, and topography is the use of underground transportation. Opportunities and benefits that might derive from a research program to accelerate the development of underground excavation technology are discussed in the report *Rapid Excavation—Significance, Needs, Opportunities.* That report was prepared for the Bureau of Mines by the National Research Council's Committee on Rapid Excavation, with partial funding provided by the Department of Housing and Urban Development and other federal agencies.

Planning for Urban Land Use Change of urban land use should follow an over-all plan developed within a policy acceptable to those living in the community. The plans of the several jurisdictions in a metropolitan area and of a region should be in general harmony. Plans for public services that require land, such as parks, golf courses, schools, and roads should be specific, and the land purchased or reserved as far in advance of established need as possible. The price of land tends to rise by more than 6 percent per year; however, money can usually be borrowed for less than 6 percent. Later purchase could be very expensive if in the meantime the land has been developed for some other function. Purchase of virgin land also eliminates the problem of dispossessing families, with the resultant hardships, high costs, and political difficulties.

A concept developed in the late 1920's might be of help in this connection. Under that concept, once a decision is reached that a school, a park, a road, or another public facility should be built in a particular location, a public declaration would be made by the local government. Following that declaration date, no change in existing private use or structures on that land is permitted. The owner or owners do not receive money for values created by the declaration. Rather, payment is based on the permitted land-use value at the time of declaration or actual use value, whichever is greater. Landowners may continue using the land until it is purchased by the community.

Not so long ago it was believed that local communities could be planned around an elementary and a high school, and groups of local communities could be tributary to a local junior college. Community size and growth patterns may now be more dependent on employment opportunities affected by transport capacity as industry migrates to the suburbs or interjects itself in or near residential areas. However, schools or the equivalent continue to serve as a focal point for developing a consciousness of neighborhood. If possible, local street patterns should complement freeway or major thoroughfare patterns to help create a physical basis for neighborhoods. An improved cost–benefit relationship may be possible when schools or other public buildings are developed as multi-use structures suitable for several community services in addition to their primary function.

Rezoning Shortcomings in the current methods by which land is zoned interfere with efficient planning. Everywhere, the procedures seem to be controversial, ineffective, and generally unsatisfactory.

New approaches should be explored. The following is offered as an example. Owners or prospective owners of a given piece of land might apply for changes in zoning that result in increased density of use and therefore in increased value. The first to apply for changes in zoning that will increase land values is likely to be the one who receives the greatest benefit from the increased value even though the increase in value is a function of the service provided by the community. Because the community provides roads, schools, sewers and water, police protection, and other services, a farm area proposed for residential rezoning can become a potentially desirable area, and after rezoning the value can change from farm value to residential value. Since much of the value added is created by the community through expenditure of community funds, the community should have opportunity to recoup its expenditures for such services.

Some recouping of funds is possible under the present system. For instance, the installation of sewer and water services is likely to be charged to the property owner. Some street costs become a part of the initial cost of the property, because the community usually requires the developer to include the construction of streets in his development plans. But, in general, most personal services, such as schools, libraries, police, and fire protection, which must be available to new residents, are not charged against the property. The owners of already existing properties pay for the establishment of those services and public facilities that a new resident would expect to find available. This means that those whose land is rezoned enjoy the value added in services provided by the community. These added values are paid for twice, once by the purchaser of rezoned property and again when the taxpayers receive their bills. The owner of rezoned property thus gains, and the community loses an opportunity for assistance in financing essential services and facilities.

This shortcoming might be reduced either by charging enough for rezoning to compensate the community for the cost of the additional facilities that must be provided, or by selling the right to rezone in a competitive market, for instance, by auctioning rezoning rights in areas in which the plan permits or calls for higher-density use. The minimum price allowed under such an auction system could be the capital cost to the community of the service that the community will be called upon to provide as a result of the change in zoning. There are other possible solutions; this is mentioned as only one that might be investigated.

Research Recommendations in the Area of Land Use and Community Development   It is recommended the Department of Housing and Urban Development examine the opportunities and techniques for meaningful studies to seek answers to the following questions:

1. What are the opportunities and means for encouraging local jurisdictions to increase local tax revenues that will enable them to assume greater local responsibility for community development?

2. Is it possible to develop national criteria for reasonable local effort of taxing and borrowing to serve as a basis for determining when assistance through federal or state subsidy is justified?

3. What mechanisms might be developed to improve the coordination of planning between regional, metropolitan, and local jurisdictions? As a part

of the cooperative effort between these jurisdictions, to what extent is it feasible for one community to obtain payment from the citizens of another community for services rendered?

4. Is the sale or auctioning of zoning privileges a feasible measure by which local jurisdictions might recapture costs of publicly financed facilities and services?

5. What additional measures are needed to help local communities reserve land sufficiently in advance of projected public need and thus avoid payment for values the community adds or values subsequently invested in land to be reserved?

6. What additional measures are needed to develop a free flow within and between the inner city and the suburbs?

7. Is it feasible to replace property taken for public use with equivalent property at a new location, if requested? If so, what norms should govern?

8. What steps can be taken by the Department of Housing and Urban Development to draft model enabling-legislation to assist agencies of local government to modernize local laws and regulations that impede the development and implementation of needed urban programs?

4

Housing and Public
Facilities and Services

The development and application of technology to urban housing and public facilities and services should be guided by clear and consistent definitions of needs. This will then permit a logical selection of technologies for competitive evaluation in applications to satisfy the stated needs. As noted earlier in this report, selection and application of technology can only occur after the social benefits desired are specified explicitly.

HOUSING

Research and development for housing and the relation of such research to the urban complex are not single-mission kinds of endeavor. The optimum process cannot be proved in the laboratory, nor is a single solution acceptable to all persons.

More significantly, there is a substantial gap between the cost of housing for those in the low-income bracket and the portion of their income that can be allocated to meet their housing needs. In the case of a family of four with one wage earner working a 40-hour week and receiving the present minimum wage, whose housing needs might be satisfied by an apartment of approximately 1,000 square feet, the ratio of cost to ability to pay is approximately 3 to 1. Nearly half of the total housing cost is associated with administrative and financial burdens. Of the actual construction cost, 70 to 75 percent is represented by labor and the remainder by material.

The dilemma posed by this economic gap suggests two basic approaches. Efforts must be made insofar as possible to design the type of housing that will have minimum construction and administrative costs for those in the low-income bracket. Simultaneously, every effort should be made to upgrade family income through the development of additional skills and through employment of more than one family member. Ideally, the gap will eventually be reduced by these measures and opportunity for home ownership in the lower-income group will increase. In the interim, the upgrading of income through housing subsidies may be the only way to span the gap.

Housing Research and Development Research in housing must be long term because of its long-term implications, but it must couple with short-range efforts. Success or failure in housing must be measured in terms of years; therefore, monitoring systems for housing research programs need to be continuous.

Since housing is not a commodity that is transportable over great distances at this time, all devices presently available need to be used to reduce costs and to satisfy construction demands. All factors must be taken into account and not just those applicable to construction methods.

The Building Research Advisory Board report, *Research and Experimental Strategy for Community and Urban Excellence,* attached as Appendix A to this report, offers a schematic representation of an approach to resolving urban building and rebuilding problems. As shown graphically in the report, problems of housing need to be undertaken as a part of a comprehensive overview of all factors bearing on the problem, that is, land use and its cost, methods of construction, resources and technical capabilities in the area, community distribution, regional implications, job distribution, availability of housing, rehabilitation of old housing, new housing needs, commercial development, schooling, educational institutions, codes, and zoning. Incentives must include the profit concept, but goals must transcend the profit motive.

Probably the most important aspects of a short- and long-term research and development program for housing are the establishment of goals and objectives and the organization and management of systems for construction. These aspects bear heavily on the next most significant element—quality of the product. A vitally important consideration that cannot be physically measured is that housing must be viable and satisfying.

Research in housing conducted without inputs from the user will in most instances prove to be unsuccessful. Technological capability alone does not ensure success in the field of housing; it is but one factor in a total complex, involving education and many other factors at the human level.

Reducing Building Costs It can be seen that material technology must necessarily play a relatively minor role in any scheme to reduce building costs if one examines fully the variety of related external and internal factors involved in the total costs for housing. Technology has its greatest cost-reducing impact in those instances where it can accelerate the building process, thus cutting labor costs; however, this approach will not necessarily have a major effect in reducing total costs. If significant cost reduction is to be achieved, greater effort is needed to develop improved techniques for management and decision-making and to eliminate existing constraints in financing methods, building codes, zoning procedures, and other outmoded regulations.

Inherent in the confusion that prevails in a housing industry that is fractured into many subsections is the lack of design criteria and documentation of performance. Although many data are available, the substructural arrangement has not produced a data-collection system from which a progressive buildup of criteria might be developed. Decision-makers have been forced to rely on crude predictors because of inherited procedures in a craft-oriented industry. There is urgent need for the housing industry to employ additional research and development talent that will enhance innovation and stimulate intellectual challenge.

Many in the building industry believe that building code specifications are a barrier to cost reduction and should be replaced with the performance requirements concept. Introduction of this concept has been delayed for several reasons. For example, performance requirements are not easily delineated, performance standards are not readily defined, and standard evaluation techniques have not yet been developed. The latter should not be allowed to delay the use of the performance requirements concept as there are many experienced professionals within metropolitan or state areas who could join together in rendering judgments of performance requirements based on their collective expertise. Such groups assembled at critical points in the nation could speed up the implementation of performance criteria by providing the evaluation service needed. The Department should keep abreast of developments in this area and support timely and meaningful research projects.

Up to this time, industrialized housing efforts have not proved competitive with on-site construction, primarily because the market for housing in any specific area has not been sufficient as to volume and time. The limited market, in conjunction with the cost of financing, code requirements, the added costs of transportation to the site and labor costs at the site, has in the past made the factory mass-produced house uneconomical. However, this does not mean that the concept should be discarded. The speed at which urban areas are developing, the constant shift in the centers of population, and the changes taking place in transportation might well have an impact that will change the market to one in which mass production of housing would be applicable. The Committee invites attention to a special report by the Building Research Advisory Board, *Historical Evaluation of Industrialized Housing and Building Systems.* The BRAB report indicates that industrialization in housing has progressed over the years and that the technical knowledge needed for effective industrialization of the housing industry to achieve large-scale mass production now exists. Extracts from this BRAB report are given in Appendix B.

Research Recommendations in the Area of Housing The following recommendations are made regarding research in the area of housing:

1. Research and development programs concerned with improving the housing situation in the context of community development must, as a first step, identify common objectives and goals so that all levels of government can cooperate in their achievement and the necessary resources of the private sector, particularly the knowledge and experience in housing, construction, and management, can be applied in a coordinated effort to seek solutions to housing problems. Specific project examples are the following:

a. What limits in number of family units should be placed in low-income clusters? At what stage do they become candidates for decay?

b. What factors—including legal, governmental, regulatory, and financial—are involved in zonal mixing of low-income and medium-income units? Is there a need to ensure that low-income units do not erode the value and equity of medium-income living space? Should there be a counterpart of the Federal Deposit Insurance mechanism?

2. The urban research and development action program should be structured to achieve good communications and cooperation between the various jurisdictions, it must possess the flexibility to bring the best minds of the communities and the nation to bear on urban problems, and it must be supported by adequate funds to encourage action.

3. Urban research and development programs should support community improvement and the participation of viable younger groups in the community.

4. Research projects must be done within the context of the user, considering all the implications of social interrelationships and human values.

5. The Department should exercise leadership in seeking opportunities for further developments in mass production of housing.

6. Research projects should develop means and measures to increase opportunities for more individuals to become homeowners with the option to live in either the urban area or the suburban area.

7. Research for low-cost housing should be directed toward cutting construction costs, developing new planning and space concepts, reducing closing

and administrative costs, and evaluation of tax policies, code requirements, and zoning procedures. Means for expeditious and effective rehabilitation and renovation and the reduction of land costs should also be studied. Project examples are the following:

a. Zoning, planning, codes, and administrative burdens appear to increase low-income housing costs substantially. Study by monitoring and analyzing actual projects the source and magnitude of such burdens and explore ways to reduce them.

b. There has been an increasing belief that construction labor productivity is deteriorating and that craft delineations add more to costs than specialization saves. Study by monitoring and analyzing actual projects to determine what opportunities there may be for improvements in designs and methods of construction.

c. Design studies of construction patterns that will withstand the wear imposed by typical low-income rental tenants and still meet their cultural requirements.

d. Design studies of family units suited to the living patterns of low-income families, for example, communal.

e. Analyze the relative impact and balance of simultaneously providing new low-income units, upgrading existing low- to medium-income units thus freeing lower-cost housing for the less advantaged, refurbishing outdated units, upgrading and refurbishing with some geographic movement within the inner city or to the industrial–commercial area of employment. What combination offers the best cost–effectiveness?

f. Abandoned furnishings, automobiles, and structures (stores, garages, filling stations, and tenements) represent a form of trash that has a deteriorating influence on a neighborhood. Study how such forms of trash can be removed by establishing legal requirements, regulatory requirements, tax incentives, or other means.

g. Observation of many neighborhoods indicates that good maintenance provides incentives to neighbors to do likewise and, conversely, that decay and misuse tend to spread. Study the pivotal balance that is needed to avoid deterioration.

PUBLIC FACILITIES AND SERVICES

Public facilities and services (and related activities) may be categorized as those the resident must ordinarily seek beyond his home (for example, health, education, and recreation), or those that are customarily brought directly to the resident (for example, energy, water, and waste disposal). In a sense, the first category consists of discretionary services and the second one of nondiscretionary services.

Separating services into these two broad categories makes it possible to consider each category as a whole, as well as interactions within and between each—to view the services as a system. If services are studied singly, there is a tendency to give undue emphasis to one or several services out of context with the whole system. A coordinated approach is also beneficial in bringing into quick focus the many facets of urban problems, thus permitting the establishment of priorities more readily. It also provides a simple way of testing the hypothesis that a successful attack on blight on a massive scale requires integrating the solutions to social problems with solutions to "brick and mortar" problems.

In both categories of services, a mechanism is needed to implement the research at the lowest possible cost without jeopardizing the orderly and effective acquisition of knowledge or the philosophy of a coordinated approach.

Equally applicable to both categories of services is the principle of avoiding design obsolescence. When expensive long-lived facilities are constructed it is desirable to forecast future technological developments and make provision for their subsequent incorporation into the facilities. The Departmental staff should therefore include personnel competent in the forecasting of technology.

Discretionary Services The concept of an all-purpose center for discretionary services is believed worthy of further study. Such a center could provide a focus for community interests and be as much an urban research laboratory as a servant of the community, as much an educational tool for the urbanologist as for the community resident, as much a nucleus for developing community political power as a cradle for establishing local democratic institutions, as much a home for advanced urban studies and social action as an ideal place for recreation and leisure-time activities. Its location should be such that the center would serve as a hub for rebuilding an entire community, with the first rehabilitation and urban renewal of housing occurring around its periphery and growing outward. There are community centers serving various groups in various communities today; however, none are known to be designed to operate as broadly and as a living laboratory as discussed here.

Community Service Center Concept Community service centers serving a large group of people—perhaps 25,000 or 50,000, the optimum number to be determined by research and demonstration—could be designed to house, in one or more buildings and surroundings, combinations of the following kinds of services:

> medical (diagnostic, preventive, remedial);
> educational (for all ages—academic and vocational);
> recreational (indoor and outdoor);
> welfare and other social services;
> community administration;
> police and fire protection;
> legal and judicial; and
> banking and commercial.

The community service center concept is suggested as an experimental research project to examine the effect of centralized services and facilities on community relationships. A center of this type might prove to be the showcase of the neighborhood or community it serves—the link to a better life in a desirable environment. It might serve as a clearing center for urban research. An early stage of the research program undertaken to explore the service center concept should seek appropriate layouts and combinations of facilities within structures that best serve the needs of selected urban communities.

While helping to satisfy current and emerging needs, the community service center approach offers a research device by which studies could be undertaken, seeking answers to many questions similar to the following:

1. What role does upgrading discretionary services play in raising the quality of life in the community and satisfying aspirations?

2. Can the community govern itself and live in harmony, given the appropriate mechanism and a base upon which to grow?

3. Can research capabilities be strengthened and results made more useful by conducting continuing experiments in real-life situations and in an environment designed for such activities?

4. Can community subcenters play a useful role?

5. Can a community service center serve as a source of information and an organized mechanism for determining residents' needs, desires, and problems? Plans for such a study should include steps to ensure that a system is developed by which information useful to the management, operations, and relations of the community is disseminated.

6. What are the advantages or disadvantages if social workers, urban trainees, and others learning and participating in the community revitalization process are housed in a residential environment within a community center?

7. What opportunities are offered under the community service center concept to study new and more efficient judicial procedures, with a view to

increasing respect for the law and providing the highest standards of fairness?

8. What are the advantages and disadvantages of providing flexible floor space in buildings? What are the acceptable mechanisms in providing flexible space? Does the community service center offer opportunities for evaluating new building technology?

9. Are there ways of allocating costs (rent) for multifunctional activities so that public facilities for the more affluent may carry more of the cost burden than the less affluent tenants of the center?

10. Can the community service center concept enhance police–community relationships?

11. Is it feasible to include educational facilities within a community service center to help those who wish to help themselves by teaching them to become businessmen, to train for desirable jobs, to improve their skills, and to help them learn to deal with the world outside their community as well as with problems within the community?

12. What are the advantages associated with a community service center serving as a nucleus for pooled transportation to points within and outside the community as may be needed for access to employment or for other defined purposes?

13. Do real estate values on the periphery of a community service center rise? Does such a center encourage private investment and create a catalytic effect?

14. What is the effect of raising the level of services without raising the quality of housing in the community? Such a question might be tested in at least one instance.

As with model cities, the entire center planning should be done first. Implementation can be accomplished on a phase basis if sufficient funds are not immediately available. However, the pooling of many facilities opens the possibility of obtaining available funds from many agencies. Since part of the research is to determine the synergistic effect of combining facilities in one center or complex, institutions such as hospitals, post offices, theaters, universities, department stores, utilities, and libraries should be encouraged to open branches or base primary operations in the area of the center. To this end, the first centers should be built where such alliances are most likely.

Nondiscretionary Services The broad concept of a multipurpose utility "tunnel" or facility is believed to be one that should be studied and evaluated, full scale, in several communities and in several variations.

Basic questions that might be studied in the utility tunnel concepts are—

1. Can water, energy, communication, waste disposal, and other services

be combined in such fashion to lower capital and operating costs while improving service for the present and the future?

2. What capacity upgrading within the initial construction will be the most economical?

3. What reconstruction will become necessary during the expected load growth of the area served?

Research and development in the area of nondiscretionary services must be intensified. Some of the kinds of innovations that might be further developed include the following:

1. Leasing or renting of space within utility tunnels, condominium style, as a means of spreading costs;

2. Improving accessibility for ease of maintenance and addition of supplementary services;

3. Providing chilled water for air conditioning to all, as a utility, to spread costs over the broadest possible base and to test the social benefits of this concept;

4. Providing maintenance services such as painting, appliance repair, and other home needs, on a mass basis, or combined with the initial contract for new construction or rehabilitation; also, the establishing of local maintenance businesses run by the community;

5. Providing an opportunity to utility companies to expand the scope of their operations and services. Profit incentives might be offered in return for investing funds for an increased level of research and development in the area of combination services; and

6. Disposing of waste (mechanically or chemically) as close as possible to the source of generation, or by transporting it to a distant point. The subject of waste disposal should be evaluated more systematically than has been done to date, and alternative approaches for the removal of all waste from the community should be studied in terms of dollars per person, dollars per ton, and dollars per unit of time.

The relationship of services in a given community or neighborhood to that of its surrounding communities should be taken into consideration in studies that the Department undertakes. In this regard, any utility tunnel studies should be done with the cooperation of the state or county level. Public or quasi-public authority and other mechanisms should also be studied to determine the optimum method for assigning responsibility for total services.

Urban Transportation Technology Urban transportation, involving both goods and people, is a crucial element in the over-all urban problem and much work in this area has already been carried out. Some significant publications bearing on this problem area are the following:

Conference on New Approaches to Urban Transportation. Report of a conference sponsored by the Department of Housing and Urban Development, Statler Hilton Hotel, Washington, D.C., November 27, 1967.

Cars for Cities. A study of trends in the design of vehicles with particular reference to their use in towns. Reports of the Steering Group and Working Group, Ministry of Transport. Her Majesty's Stationery Office, London, 1967.

The Automobile and Air Pollution, Program for Progress (Part 1). Report of Panel on Electrically Powered Vehicles to Commerce Technical Advisory Board, October 1967.

Design and Performance Criteria for Improved Nonrail Mass Transit Vehicles and Related Urban Transportation Systems. Report to the Department of Housing and Urban Development prepared by the Highway Research Board, National Research Council, for the Academy of Engineering, Washington, D.C., May 1968.

Technology and Urban Transporation. Report prepared by Robert U. Ayres, Hudson Institute, Croton-on-Hudson, New York, 1968.

These studies show that the contribution of the transportation industry toward the solution of urban problems is not so much limited by technology as by economic factors.*

There is general agreement that a balanced system of rail-guided and independently controlled vehicles will be required, and only actual experience with some of the systems already being constructed will indicate the proper direction for further experiments in this area. In general, rail transit in some form will serve best in areas of high population density such as Manhattan but is ineffective or uneconomical in regions where the population is dispersed.

In this area of study a series of carefully chosen relatively large-scale experiments will be required, with each being carefully evaluated before and during construction and after several years of operation. The advantages of rail transit in any of its various forms are high carrying capacity for peak periods and relatively low labor costs in the operating phase. The disadvantages are high initial costs, low over-all utilization rate, and lack of flexibility in responding to changing needs of the community it is expected to serve.

Nonrail vehicles, including helicopters, are available in a bewildering variety of forms. Vehicles of any of the various kinds can be effective, however,

*See *Proceedings of Institute of Electrical and Electronics Engineers,* Vol. 56, No. 4, April 1968, pp. 377-786.

only if suitably chosen to serve as part of some properly designed over-all system. We know much more about vehicles and power plants than we do about systems, so it is for this reason that in the current situation it is research on systems, rather than on vehicles, that is needed. With systems, only relatively large-scale, long-term experiments will give the kinds of data that are needed.

The over-all situation with respect to transportation systems is not much different from that which faced the Atomic Energy Commission when various power-reactor concepts were being invented faster than they could be evaluated. To break this impasse, the "reactor of the year" demonstration program was started. A similar series of experiments with a "transportation system of the year" would surely go far toward resolving the current confusion in urban transportation. Only a program of such scope would permit experiments on a scale adequate to give significant results in a field as complex as that of urban transportation, where separation of variables is proving to be next to impossible.

Suggestions for a wide variety of experiments of this type were made by a panel of the Department of Housing and Urban Development–Office of Science and Technology Summer Study on Science and Urban Development, 1966. Among those suggestions given high priority were—

1. Jitneys with dynamic scheduling,
2. Improvement of present buses,
3. Aids to relieve core city congestion,
4. Control systems for major corridors,
5. Pedestrian aids, and
6. Rail transport improvements.

An additional topic recommended by this Committee is the effect of vehicle reliability and driver reliability on the design of major arteries.

The helicopter and likely future developments in vertical take-off and landing (VTOL) aircraft were not included among the suggestions in the HUD/OST Summer Study. These vehicles should not be neglected, however, as they are significant developments to which cities must adjust in connection with the flow of goods into and out of congested areas. Certain of these suggestions have been accepted and the government is funding work in these areas. Examples are studies on the Urbmobile at Cornell Aeronautical Laboratory, on the Commucar and PERC (personal capsules) at M.I.T., and on electric cars in general for the Philadelphia central business district at the University of Pennsylvania. As reports come in from such initial studies, it will be possible to focus more effectively on the next phase of the research program. Based on results available to date, effort might well be directed to experiments with express lanes for buses; with the dial-a-bus approach; with low pollutant, low-noise power plants for buses; and with dual-mode concepts.

Factors That Will Dominate the Use of Transport Services   There are three major factors that determine the place of transportation in urban technology. Effective planning should take these factors into careful account:

1. *Rising Real Family Income.* The percentage of families with income under $3,000 in constant 1966 dollars dropped by over 50 percent from 1947 to 1966. Median incomes rose 68 percent in this 20-year period. The income of Negro families rose more rapidly than that of white. The median income of Negro families was 51.2 percent of that of white families in 1947, and 59.6 percent of that of white families in 1966, an increase of about one-sixth in the ratio of Negro-to-white income during this period.

While the median income was growing by more than two-thirds in constant dollars, the income received by the lowest quintile rose more than 80 percent.* This suggests that the annual rate of growth of the income of the lowest quintile has been about 3 percent in constant dollars, while the median income has been rising about 2.75 percent per year in constant dollars. Transportation planning should not assume that the income of the lowest group will rise at a much faster rate than this, or that median incomes will rise faster than this, in the next decade.

Transportation fares without subsidy apparently have reached the limit for the lowest quintile, but they have not necessarily reached the limit for the other quintiles.

2. *Rising Living Standards.* Living standards are rising in terms both of personal consumption and of the environment expected by workers, even among the lowest quintile. Successive data from the housing censuses have continued to show a marked decrease in the number of substandard housing units, and the last Economic Report suggests a sizable decline between 1960 and 1966. In working spaces, too, air conditioning, improved lighting, better elevator service, and more attractive quarters are necessary if office workers are to be retained these days.

Rising standards accompany increases in real income, and transportation standards must rise with improvements elsewhere. Rail, bus, and auto services must improve, or they will lose their clientele. Workers who were willing to stand to get to and from their jobs 30 years ago are less and less willing to stand now. Such factors as comfort, convenience, reliability, and speed are increasingly important to people traveling in metropolitan areas.

*Data on family income are taken from Bureau of Labor Statistics report No. 332 and Current Population report Series P-23, No. 24. The data on the lowest quintile come from Census Consumer Income, P-60, No. 53, Table J.

3. *Technical Factors.* The centers of most cities developed during a period in which transportation and communication technologies were relatively primitive. Current technologies make it easier for industry and commerce to move and disperse to the suburbs. They make it possible to have one-story factory buildings with adequate parking, greenery, and pleasant office space as a part of the complex. Commercial centers can be scattered around residential areas, can provide adequate parking space, and can possess the attributes of small parks. Residential areas can have sizable lots and still be near school, work, shopping, and play. A transportation breakthrough has been achieved for urban planning and development. The bus and the automobile have given mobility to the average family, and it is no longer necessary to live close to the streetcar or close to work. Families can spread out, have space, and still conveniently reach shopping centers at some distance from their homes. The freedom of workers to choose their place and even the hours of employment has increased the need for adjustability in transportation systems.

a. *Handicaps of Rail Transportation.* Transportation must provide the adaptability that will enable industry and commerce to serve their customers. This requirement creates a technical obstacle to the long-continued use of rail transportation. Residents of suburban areas formerly traveled downtown effectively by rail. But as the automobile moved people farther from the immovable rail lines, buses had to take over. The combination of bus and rail or of automobile and rail was not as flexible as a bus or an automobile-and-bus system would have been, and business has had to move closer to the customer.

In addition to its inflexibility, rail has a second important disadvantage in urban transportation. It requires mass volume at both pickup and discharge points. A train is a very expensive piece of equipment. To be profitable, it must carry a large number of people. If it stops to discharge just a few people, there is a heavy capital charge and a substantial time loss to passengers still en route to their destinations. Because the urban train and its roadbed are used effectively for only a few hours of the day, rail capital costs per passenger mile are higher than bus capital costs per passenger mile at comparable volumes.

Urban rail systems have a third important handicap. Trains carry many people from one single point to some other single point. Buses that can carry 50,000 passengers per lane per hour avoid this handicap in highway lanes reserved for buses, for they can carry passengers going only to a specific area. Trains must stop at several points on the way, but the bus can go by such points until it comes to the area where its passengers want to stop. The bus can maintain a steady 35-mile-an-hour pace with only several bus lengths between its taillight and the bumper of the following bus. When it reaches its destination, it can turn off while the buses following continue to other destinations.

   b. Handicaps of Nonrail Vehicles. Rubber-tired vehicles have their handicaps as well. At least three important constraints to the use of automobiles and buses must be remembered in planning transport capacity or laying out new urban areas:

   (1) Parking space per office worker transported by automobile may be as great as the office space required per worker. This will vary, of course, with the classification of the worker, but when workers drive to their offices in private vehicles, large areas must be reserved for parking. Residential parking in apartment house areas is also a critical issue.

   (2) Although automobiles provide independence and flexibility, they require more total space per passenger than do buses and rails. As the number of automobiles increases on any given origin–destination pattern, the capability of bus service as a space-saving alternative should be kept in mind.

   (3) The third and, at the moment, most serious problem involved in the use of rubber-tired vehicles is air pollution. This will be reduced by future technology; meanwhile, keeping the vehicles moving can make the largest contribution toward reducing pollution from the source.

Recommendations in the Area of Public Facilities and Services   With respect to research in the area of public facilities and services, it is recommended—

   1. That the community center concept for locating discretionary services be studied and evaluated as a possible means for obtaining the necessary community focus and as a mechanism for community-related research undertakings. The study should also explore the concept in terms of urban transportation services. For example, will transportation flow be best suited by a central cluster with satellites or by selective combinations at somewhat different locations?

   2. That the broad concept of a multipurpose utility tunnel be studied and evaluated on a full-scale basis in several communities and in several variations to establish whether water, energy, communication, waste disposal, and other utility services can be combined therein in such a fashion to lower operating costs and improve service. The cooperation of the state and county should be solicited in such a study. Further, public or quasi-public authority should be examined as a part of the study to determine the optimum way in which to vest responsibility for total services.

   3. That steps be taken to encourage universities to develop programs for training in the development and management of utilities and services as a system.

4. That a series of carefully chosen large-scale experiments be undertaken to explore the significant implications and applications of balanced systems of rail-guided and independently controlled vehicles for use in urban areas. Each experimental system must be carefully evaluated before construction as well as during and after several years of operation.

5. That, in all planning, the probability of improvements in short-haul aircraft technology be kept in focus. The helicopter is here, and other VTOL vehicles will be developed within the decade, and they will add a new dimension to opportunities for transportation of both goods and people.

Appendix A

Research and Experimental Strategy for Community and Urban Excellence (RESCUE)

Prepared by the Committee on Rehabilitation and Urbanization, Building Research Advisory Board

INTRODUCTION

In the Fall of 1966, the Building Research Advisory Board, during discussion with government officials, requested its Committee on Rehabilitation and Urbanization to develop a strategy for applying research and technology to the problems of urban building and rebuilding. The Committee deliberations resulted in a broad outline of the elements and their interrelationships, considered to be essential to a systematic and rational approach to the problem.

In April 1967, the outline was first made available by BRAB to a limited number of government officials in a rather unpolished form—because of expressed urgency it was accomplished in the very short time of six weeks. In light of the repeated requests for copies since that time, the Board believes that the Committee's effort could help to crystallize the task ahead of solving the nation's community problems, and thus it is making that outline available for the use of others.

This report comprises a preliminary outline of considerations and relationships essential to establishing a strategy for application of research and technology to the problems of urban building and rebuilding.

The outline was structured using as bases two possible approaches to strategy development—one is sequential, the other is dynamic. Since urban technology problems must be addressed quickly, the Committee agreed that neither available time nor funds would permit full implementation of a sequential approach. Consequently, the major effort was directed toward development of the dynamic approach in which the various steps can be taken simultaneously. The outlined steps include the establishment of empirical goals, identification of constraints, initiation of demonstrations to hasten trial feedback, and the establishment of evaluative techniques and cost–effectiveness programs.

Interrelationships of the various steps require detailed study and refinement. Yet, if a major goal is to be set, such as broad achievement of a better urban life for all with emphasis particularly on improved low-income housing, a complete matrix relating all pertinent social and cost factors must be evolved and the adjustments made to meet the constantly changing relationships of participants. Only then can reasonable priorities be established and decisions made as to what research and experimentation is needed and which segment of each might best be carried on by public or private sectors. Decision-making is not as important at this time as construction of the cost–effectiveness and constraint-minimization matrix, for which this outline is only the beginning.

BUILDING RESEARCH ADVISORY BOARD

COMMITTEE ON REHABILITATION AND URBANIZATION

JOSEPH H. NEWMAN, *Chairman;* Tishman Research Corporation
GLEN H. BEYER, Cornell University
PATRICK CONLEY, Office of Science and Technology
EDWARD T. HALL, Illinois Institute of Technology
C. THEODORE LARSON, University of Michigan
WILLIAM J. McSORLEY, Building and Construction Trades Department, AFL-CIO
ROBINSON NEWCOMB, Consulting Economist
JOHN S. PARKINSON, Johns-Manville Research and Engineering Center
HERBERT H. SWINBURNE, Nolen, Swinburne and Associates

SEQUENTIAL APPROACH

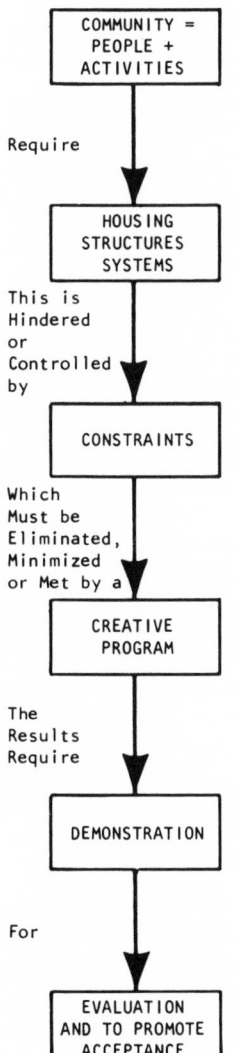

DYNAMIC APPROACH

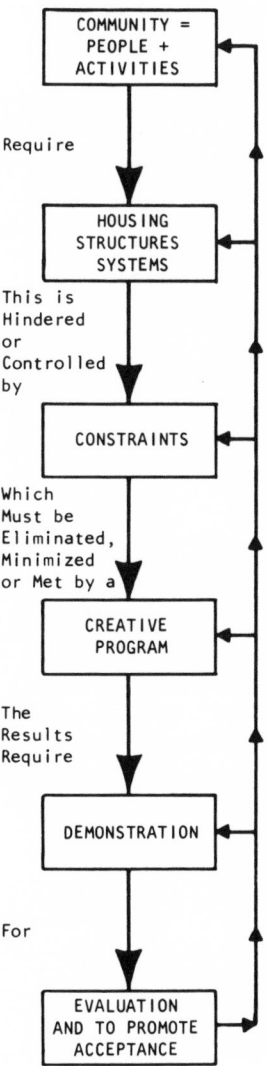

SEQUENTIAL APPROACH

DEFINE WHAT PEOPLE HAVE, WANT, NEED AND CAN AFFORD.

ESTABLISH GOALS.

DETERMINE MEANS AND COSTS OF ACHIEVING GOALS.

DEFINE CONSTRAINTS.

MEASURE THE TOTAL EFFECT OF CONSTRAINTS ON MEANS AND COST OF ACHIEVING GOALS.

ESTABLISH CREATIVE PROGRAM.

MEASURE THE EFFECT OF CREATIVE PROGRAM ON MINIMIZING CONSTRAINTS.

DEMONSTRATE RESULTS OF CREATIVE PROGRAM.

EVALUATE DEMONSTRATION.

IN THIS APPROACH EACH STEP AWAITS THE RESULTS OF THE PREVIOUS ONE. THE DYNAMIC NATURE OF URBANIZATION AND THE URGENCY OF ACHIEVING THE STATED GOALS REQUIRE A DYNAMIC (SIMULTANEOUS) INSTEAD OF A SYSTEMATIC (SEQUENTIAL) APPROACH.

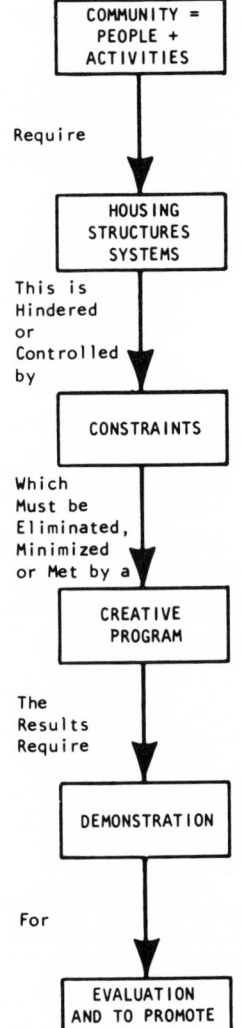

COMMUNITY = PEOPLE + ACTIVITIES

Require

HOUSING STRUCTURES SYSTEMS

This is Hindered or Controlled by

CONSTRAINTS

Which Must be Eliminated, Minimized or Met by a

CREATIVE PROGRAM

The Results Require

DEMONSTRATION

For

EVALUATION AND TO PROMOTE ACCEPTANCE

DYNAMIC
APPROACH

ESTABLISH EMPIRICAL GOALS (3 LEVELS OF EXCELLENCE--
MINIMUM, INTERMEDIATE, MAXIMUM) UNTIL RESEARCH
REVEALS REAL GOALS.

IDENTIFY CONSTRAINTS AND ESTABLISH EMPIRICAL LEVELS
OF CONSTRAINT TOLERANCE AS BASIC TARGETS FOR
CREATIVE PROGRAM UNTIL REAL SIGNIFICANCE OF
CONSTRAINTS IS MEASURED.

IMMEDIATELY INITIATE SEVERAL DEMONSTRATION AND
CREATIVE PROJECTS, BASED ON JUDGMENT, TO HASTEN
FEEDBACK.

ESTABLISH BASES FOR EVALUATION AND EVALUATIVE
TECHNIQUES TOGETHER WITH A SYSTEM FOR CONTINUOUS
AND CONTINUING MEASUREMENT OF ACHIEVEMENT.

ESTABLISH A COST EFFECTIVENESS PROGRAM TO
DETERMINE PRIORITIES FOR CREATIVE AND DEMONSTRATION
PROJECTS, FIRST USING EMPIRICAL DATA, THEN REAL
INFORMATION.

CONTINUOUSLY ADJUST, MODIFY AND SUPPLEMENT PROGRAMS
AS INFORMATION EVOLVES. WHEREVER POSSIBLE,
DEMONSTRATE SIMULTANEOUSLY SEVERAL RESULTS OF
CREATIVE PROGRAM.

NOTE: BE PREPARED TO WRITE OFF SOME FAILURES.
        NEGATIVE FINDINGS CAN PROVIDE USEFUL
        INFORMATION.

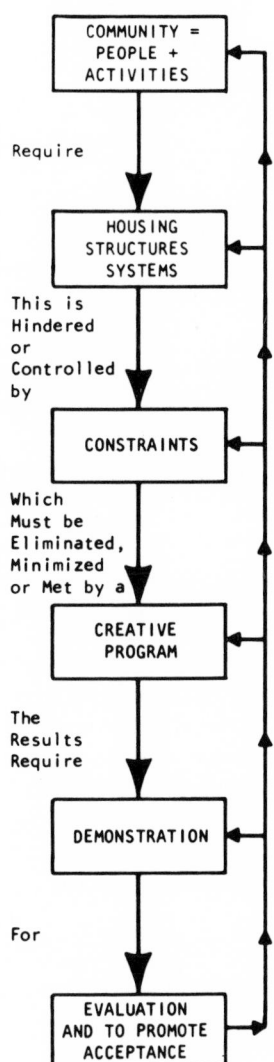

COMMUNITY =
PEOPLE +
ACTIVITIES

Require

HOUSING
STRUCTURES
SYSTEMS

This is
Hindered
or
Controlled
by

CONSTRAINTS

Which
Must be
Eliminated,
Minimized
or Met by a

CREATIVE
PROGRAM

The
Results
Require

DEMONSTRATION

For

EVALUATION
AND TO PROMOTE
ACCEPTANCE

SOME EXAMPLES OF EMPIRICAL
GOALS WHICH MIGHT BE SET

2% REDUCTION IN RENT OR CARRYING CHARGES FOR
OCCUPANT EACH YEAR COMMENCING 1969, FOR A
CUMULATIVE REDUCTION OF 14% BY 1975.

2% INCREASE IN VALUE OF SERVICES, QUALITY OF
LIVING, AND RESOURCES EACH YEAR COMMENCING 1969,
FOR A CUMULATIVE INCREASE OF 14% BY 1975.

REPLACEMENT OR REHABILITATION OF 30% OF
SUBSTANDARD HOUSING AND ENVIRONMENT BY 1975.

A SUBSTANTIAL INCREASE IN CREATIVE PROGRAMS AND
COOPERATION BY PRIVATE ENTERPRISE.

PRIORITIES

TO SET PRIORITIES, A PROGRAM FOR DETERMINATION OF
COST/SOCIAL EFFECTIVENESS MUST BE ESTABLISHED AND
CONTINUALLY UPDATED.

IN DOLLARS ESTABLISH:

1. NET POTENTIAL EFFECT OF EACH CONSTRAINT REMOVAL
    OR MINIMIZATION

    A. REDUCTION IN COST OF HOUSING AND SERVICES

    B. INCREASE IN PRODUCTIVITY

    C. POTENTIAL GAIN IN EARNING POWER

    D. INCREASE IN STANDARD OF LIVING

    E. INCREASE IN QUALITY OR PERFORMANCE

    F. ETC.

    _____

    TOTAL $ SAVED

THERE MAY BE SOME NEGATIVE EFFECTS, WHICH VALUE
SHOULD BE DEBITED IN ACHIEVING THE NET POTENTIAL
SAVINGS.

2. COST OF CREATIVE PROGRAM TO MINIMIZE OR REMOVE
    CONSTRAINT, I.E., DOLLARS TO BE SPENT.

3. $\frac{\text{ITEM 1}}{\text{ITEM 2}} = \frac{\text{\$ SAVED}}{\text{\$ SPENT}}$ = POTENTIAL ULTIMATE

    COST EFFECTIVENESS.

4. COST OF DEMONSTRATION.

5. POTENTIAL INFLUENCE OF DEMONSTRATION ON REMOVAL
    OR MINIMIZATION.

6. $\frac{\text{ITEM 5}}{\text{ITEM 4}} = \frac{\text{\$ SAVED}}{\text{\$ SPENT}}$ = POTENTIAL IMMEDIATE

    COST EFFECTIVENESS.

7. $\frac{\text{ITEM 6}}{\text{ITEM 5}} = \frac{\text{POTENTIAL IMMEDIATE COST EFFECTIVENESS}}{\text{POTENTIAL ULTIMATE COST EFFECTIVENESS}}$ = LEVERAGE.

COST EFFECTIVENESS SHOULD BE ESTABLISHED FOR VARYING
LEVELS OF ACHIEVEMENT.

EXAMPLE:

THROUGH A CREATIVE ALL OUT RESEARCH PROGRAM, IT IS
DETERMINED THAT THE COST OF WASTE DISPOSAL CAN BE
DECREASED, FOR EXAMPLE, BY SOME $120,000,000 OVER
AN AGREED-UPON DURATION TIME. THE COST OF THE
NECESSARY RESEARCH AND DEVELOPMENT IS ESTIMATED AT
SOME $20,000,000. THUS, THE POTENTIAL ULTIMATE COST
EFFECTIVENESS IS 6.

AN EXPENDITURE OF SOME $600,000 FOR A DEMONSTRATION
PROJECT AND/OR PROVIDING INCENTIVES TO ENCOURAGE
PRIVATE ENTERPRISE TO UNDERTAKE THE NECESSARY
ACTIVITY MAY DECREASE THE COST OF WASTE DISPOSAL,
FOR EXAMPLE, BY $30,000,000 IN THIS SAME PERIOD. ALTHOUGH
LESS IS SAVED IN DOLLARS, THE POTENTIAL IMMEDIATE
COST EFFECTIVENESS IS 50.

THE LEVERAGE IS $\frac{50}{6}$ OR 8.3.

COMPARE THIS WITH SOME $15,000,000 ALL-OUT CREATIVE
PROGRAM FOR MINIMIZING THE CONSTRAINTS IMPOSED BY
LABOR PRACTICES WHICH MAY RESULT IN A NET SAVINGS
OF SOME $300,000,000. THE POTENTIAL ULTIMATE COST
EFFECTIVENESS IN THIS EXAMPLE IS 20 (MORE THAN 3
TIMES AS EFFECTIVE AS THE FIRST EXAMPLE).

FURTHER, COMPARE THIS SITUATION, WHERE AN EXPENDI-
TURE OF SOME $300,000 FOR A CONTRACT WITH LABOR
TO EVOLVE A PLAN FOR AN EQUITABLE SOLUTION TO
PROBLEMS RESULTING FROM INNOVATIONS IN BUILDINGS,
MAY RESULT IN A SITUATION THAT WOULD ACHIEVE A
NET COST SAVINGS OF SOME $90,000,000. ALTHOUGH
LESS IS SAVED, THE POTENTIAL IMMEDIATE COST
EFFECTIVENESS IS 300 (6 TIMES AS EFFECTIVE AS THE
FIRST EXAMPLE OF A DEMONSTRATION) AND THE LEVERAGE
IS 300/20=15 (ALMOST TWICE THE LEVERAGE AS IN THE
FIRST EXAMPLE).

COMMUNITY = PEOPLE + ACTIVITIES

PEOPLE

HOW MANY?

HOW OLD ARE THEY?

WHERE DO THEY LIVE?   WHERE WOULD THEY LIKE TO LIVE?

WHAT DO THEY EARN?   WHAT WOULD THEY LIKE TO EARN?

HOW DO THEY EARN IT?   HOW WOULD THEY LIKE TO EARN THEIR LIVING?

WHAT IS THEIR FAMILY ROLE?

WHAT DO THEY POSSESS?   WHAT WOULD THEY LIKE TO POSSESS?

HOW DO THEY LIVE?   HOW WOULD THEY LIKE TO LIVE?

WHERE DO THEY WORK?   WHERE WOULD THEY LIKE TO WORK?

WHAT DO THEY DO?   WHAT WOULD THEY LIKE TO DO?

WHAT DO THEY KNOW?   WHAT WOULD THEY LIKE TO KNOW?

WHAT DO THEY NEED?   WHAT WOULD THEY LIKE TO HAVE?

WHAT ARE THEIR PROBLEMS?   WHAT ARE THEIR ASPIRATIONS?

WHAT ARE THEIR LIMITATIONS?   WHAT ARE THEIR CAPABILITIES?

WHAT ARE THEIR VALUES?

WHERE DO THEY GO?   WHERE WOULD THEY LIKE TO GO?

WHAT DO THEY DO WITH THEIR MONEY? WHAT WOULD THEY LIKE TO DO WITH THEIR MONEY?

ACTIVITIES

LIVING   WHAT IS AVAILABLE?

EDUCATIONAL   WHAT IS REQUIRED?

COMMUNICATION

HEALTH & WELFARE   WHAT IS WANTED?

RECREATIONAL   HOW SHOULD IT BE PROVIDED?

INDUSTRIAL   WHERE SHOULD IT BE?

COMMERCIAL & BUSINESS   WHAT IS THE SIGNIFICANCE?

ADMINISTRATIVE

TRANSPORTATION   WHAT DOES IT COST?

RELATIONSHIP OF PEOPLE AND ACTIVITIES TO SPACE

WHAT IS THE PRESENT RELATIONSHIP?

WHAT IS REQUIRED?

WHAT IS WANTED?

HOW SHOULD IT BE PROVIDED?

WHAT ARE THE BENEFITS?

NOTE: AS APPLICABLE, QUESTIONS
SHALL BE ANSWERED ON AN
EXPLICIT AND IMPLICIT BASIS

HOUSING STRUCTURES SYSTEMS

HOUSING

SINGLE-FAMILY
GARDEN
MIDDLE-RISE   ►NEW
HIGH-RISE
TEMPORARY
MOBILE   ►REHABILITATED
COMPOSITE
OTHER

STRUCTURES AND SYSTEMS FOR

SCHOOLS	SHOPPING CENTERS
HOSPITALS	RAILROAD STATIONS
CLINICS	BUS STATIONS
SANITATION SYSTEMS	STREETS
MEETING PLACES	CHURCHES
FIRE AND POLICE	WAREHOUSES
OFFICE BUILDINGS	HIGHWAYS
FACTORIES	PLAYGROUNDS
STORES AND SHOPS	ENERGY SYSTEMS
PARKING	COMMUNICATION
LIBRARIES	THEATRES
PARKS	LIGHTING SYSTEMS
HOTELS	LANDSCAPING
MOTELS	RAPID TRANSIT
SEWAGE	OTHERS

QUESTIONS TO BE ANSWERED CONCERNING HOUSING STRUCTURES SYSTEMS:

WHAT ARE THEY? HOW MANY?

TO WHAT STANDARDS HAVE THEY BEEN BUILT?

WHAT IS THEIR PERFORMANCE IN TERMS OF:

    QUALITY
    LIVABILITY
    REHABILITATIBILITY
    FUNCTION
    MAINTAINABILITY
    EFFICIENCY

HOW DO THEY FIT THE COMMUNITY PLAN?

WHAT DO THEY COST?

    NEW
    REPLACEMENT
    REHABILITATED
    TO MAINTAIN AND OPERATE

WHAT ARE THE ELEMENTS OF COST OF CONSTRUCTION AND OF OPERATION?

WHO OWNS THEM?

WHO MANAGES THEM?

UNDER WHAT TAXATION, ZONING, AND OTHER ADMINISTRATIVE REGULATIONS ARE THEY OPERATING?

HOW ARE THEY FINANCED?

WHAT HAS BEEN THEIR TURNOVER?

HOW ARE THEY AMORTIZED?

WHAT SYSTEMS AND TECHNIQUES HAVE BEEN USED IN THEIR CONSTRUCTION?

WHAT ARE THE TAX IMPLICATIONS OF CHANGE?

CONSTRAINTS

POLITICAL-LEGAL

TAXATION POLICIES

ZONING

CODES

REGULATIONS AND PROCEDURES

CUSTOMS

LEGISLATION

POLITICAL RAMIFICATIONS

DECISION-MAKING PROCESS

SAFETY

FIRE PREVENTION AND CONTROL

STRUCTURAL INTEGRITY

SECURITY AGAINST CRIME

PROTECTION AGAINST OTHER PERILS

HEALTH

DISEASE PREVENTION

WASTE DISPOSAL

AIR POLLUTION

COMFORT (TEMPERATURE)

NOISE

WATER SUPPLY

PHYSICAL

ENVIRONMENT

GEOGRAPHICAL LIMITATIONS

CONGESTION

AVAILABILITY OF MATERIALS AND SERVICES

CHANGING NEEDS

STRUCTURAL LONGEVITY

TRANSPORTATION

ECONOMIC

LAND COSTS

CONSTRUCTION COSTS

OPERATING COSTS

RISK

PROFITABILITY

INSURABILITY

MARKETABILITY

FINANCING CAPABILITY

FINANCING PRACTICES

SOCIAL COSTS

TECHNOLOGICAL

MANUFACTURING CAPABILITY AND PRACTICES

LABOR CAPABILITY AND PRACTICES

CONTRACTOR CAPABILITY AND PRACTICES

AVAILABILITY OF CAPITAL

SIZE OF MARKET

NATURE OF MARKET

DISTRIBUTION AND MARKETING PRACTICES

PROFESSIONAL AND SKILLED MANPOWER

CAPABILITY OF TAKING ADVANTAGE OF EXISTING TECHNOLOGY

CAPABILITY OF TAKING ADVANTAGE OF NEW TECHNOLOGY

SOCIAL

IGNORANCE

POVERTY

PERSONAL PREFERENCE

PERSONAL BEHAVIOR

JOB AVAILABILITY

LACK OF COMMUNICATION

POPULATION GROWTH AND MOVEMENT

CREATIVE PROGRAM

COST REDUCTION IS IMPLICIT

COMPONENTS AND SYSTEMS

FOUNDATION
STRUCTURE
WALLS
ELECTRICAL
PLUMBING
MECHANICAL

ENVIRONMENTAL CONTROL

WATER DISTRIBUTION
POWER DISTRIBUTION
WASTE DISPOSAL
MOVEMENT OF PEOPLE AND GOODS
COMMUNICATION SYSTEMS
AIR POLLUTION CONTROL
CLIMATE CONTROL
ENERGY SOURCES
PROTECTION AGAINST PERILS

SERVICES

MEDICAL
CRIME PREVENTION
FIRE CONTROL
EDUCATIONAL
JOB OPPORTUNITIES
CULTURAL OPPORTUNITIES
UTILIZATION OF SERVICES
STREET CLEANING

INCENTIVES

PROFITABILITY
MARKETABILITY
INSURABILITY
FINANCIBILITY
OTHER INCENTIVES

CREATIVE
PROGRAM

(Continued)

<u>EFFICIENCY</u>

FLEXIBILITY IN USE OF SPACE IN BUILDINGS

PRODUCTIVITY THROUGH STANDARDIZATION AND INDUSTRIALIZATION

VERSATILITY THROUGH MULTI-PURPOSE USE OF BUILDINGS

CAPABILITY THROUGH INCREASED PARTICIPATION OF PRIVATE ENTERPRISE AND UTILIZATION OF THEIR R & D COMPETENCE

CAPABILITY THROUGH PLAN TO SOLVE LABOR'S PROBLEMS THAT MAY EVOLVE FROM INNOVATION

UTILIZATION OF SPACE IN COMMUNITY

INTRODUCTION OF NEW CONCEPTS IN ABSENCE OF EVALUATIVE TECHNIQUES

PROCEDURES FOR ACQUIRING PROPERTY, AIR RIGHTS, AND GETTING A BUILDING PROJECT "OFF THE GROUND"

MARKETING, DISTRIBUTION AND PURCHASING PRACTICE

<u>PATTERN OF LIVING</u>

OWNERSHIP VS. LEASING

REHABILITATION VS. NEW CONSTRUCTION

PATTERNS OF FAMILY AND COMMUNITY LIVING

MOBILITY

RELOCATION PROCEDURES (TEMPORARY, PERMANENT)

COMMUNITY PLANS

INTERRELATIONSHIP OF COMMUNITY WITH OTHER COMMUNITIES

TIME ZONING (OBSOLESCENCE)

DEMONSTRATION

POSSIBLE INITIAL DEMONSTRATIONS

1. DETERMINE THE SIZE AND NATURE OF MARKET REQUIRED TO ACT AS INCENTIVE
    FOR PRIVATE ENTERPRISE TO INVEST IN R & D AND TOOLING REQUIRED TO EFFECT
    VARIOUS LEVELS OF ECONOMY AND PROVIDE CERTAIN SERVICES. PROVIDE ONE OR
    MORE DEMONSTRATION PROJECTS ON APPROPRIATE SCALE TO ILLUSTRATE MOST
    FAVORABLE SITUATION(S).

2. WORK WITH LABOR TO EVOLVE PLAN FOR EQUITABLE SOLUTION TO PROBLEMS THAT
    MAY EVOLVE FROM INNOVATION IN BUILDING AND PROVIDE A DEMONSTRATION
    PROJECT TO ILLUSTRATE EFFECTIVENESS OF PLAN.

3. ASCERTAIN VALUE OF COMBINING MAINTENANCE RESPONSIBILITY WITH INITIAL
    CONSTRUCTION RESPONSIBILITY IN HIGH RISE, LOW RISE, AND REHABILITATION
    PROJECTS.

4. ASCERTAIN VALUE OF MAXIMIZING FACTORY WORK AND MINIMIZING FIELD WORK.
    COMBINE WITH ITEM 2, IF FEASIBLE.

5. A COMMUNITY CENTER WITH MULTIPURPOSE SPACE INCORPORATING WIDE RANGE OF
    PUBLIC, COMMUNITY, AND PRIVATE FUNCTIONS (E.G., COURTS, POLICE,
    WELFARE, DIAGNOSTIC, RECREATIONAL, POST OFFICE, EDUCATIONAL, COM-
    MERICAL) TO DEMONSTRATE ECONOMICS OF NEW PATTERNS OF DISTRIBUTING COSTS
    OF SPACE, INCREASED EFFICIENCY, IMPROVED QUALITY OF SERVICES, AND
    ADVANTAGES OF FLEXIBILITY.

DEMONSTRATION

(CONTINUED)

6. OPTIMIZE DESIGN OF EACH TYPE OF HOUSING WITH AVAILABLE TECHNOLOGY;
    ESTABLISH PERFORMANCE SPECIFICATIONS; WORK WITH PRIVATE ENTERPRISE IN
    CONDUCT OF DEMONSTRATIONS (SEVERAL TEAMS) IN SITUATIONS WHERE CONSTRAINTS
    ARE PURPOSELY MINIMIZED OR ELIMINATED; EVALUATE OCCUPANT ACCEPTANCE OF
    INNOVATIONS.

7. SELECT, SAY, A DOZEN TEAMS—ARCHITECT(S), ENGINEER(S), CONTRACTOR(S),
    MANUFACTURER(S)—AND ESTABLISH A PAID COMPETITION FOR BEST ECONOMICALLY
    FEASIBLE DESIGNS (MEETING PREDETERMINED CRITERIA) IMPLEMENTED BY
    DEMONSTRATION. COMBINE WITH ITEM 6, IF FEASIBLE.

8. DEMONSTRATE IMPROVED PLUMBING SYSTEMS PREDICATED UPON FASTER AND MORE
    ECONOMICAL WAYS OF ASSEMBLY AND USE OF NEW TYPES OF MATERIAL AND FIXTURES.

9. DEMONSTRATE PRACTICABILITY OF BUILDING OVER LOW RISE BUILDINGS TO SOLVE
    RELOCATION PROBLEM AND USE SPACE THEREUNDER CONSTRUCTIVELY AFTER TENANTS
    MOVE "UPSTAIRS."

EVALUATION
AND
ACCEPTANCE

IN TERMS OF

    PERFORMANCE

    QUALITY

    COST REDUCTION

    STANDARD OF LIVING

    IMPACT ON BUSINESS

    PHYSICAL AND INTELLECTUAL RESOURCES

    CONSUMER SATISFACTION

    JOBS

    MARKET OPPORTUNITIES

    GROSS NATIONAL PRODUCT

    OTHER

THESE TERMS REQUIRE DEFINITION AND WEIGHTING.

DYNAMIC APPROACH

COMMUNITY = PEOPLE + ACTIVITIES

Require

HOUSING STRUCTURES SYSTEMS

This is Hindered or Controlled by

CONSTRAINTS

Which Must be Eliminated, Minimized or Met by a

CREATIVE PROGRAM

The Results Require

DEMONSTRATION

For

EVALUATION AND TO PROMOTE ACCEPTANCE

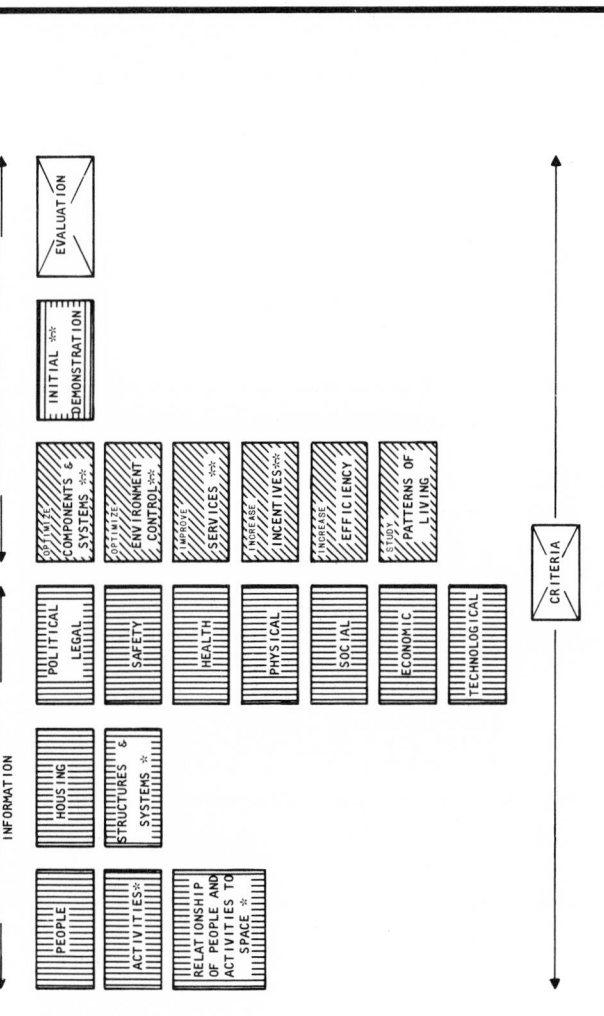

STATISTICAL-MARKET-DEMOGRAPHIC INFORMATION — HARDWARE; PROCEDURES; EVALUATION

PEOPLE

ACTIVITIES *

RELATIONSHIP OF PEOPLE AND ACTIVITIES TO SPACE *

HOUSING

STRUCTURES & SYSTEMS *

POLITICAL

LEGAL

SAFETY

HEALTH

PHYSICAL

SOCIAL

ECONOMIC

TECHNOLOGICAL

OPTIMIZE COMPONENTS & SYSTEMS **

OPTIMIZE ENVIRONMENT CONTROL **

IMPROVE SERVICES **

INCREASE INCENTIVES **

INCREASE EFFICIENCY **

STUDY PATTERNS OF LIVING

INITIAL ** DEMONSTRATION

EVALUATION

CRITERIA

Legend:

ALL SEGMENTS

PRIVATE ENTERPRISE WITH ASSISTANCE FROM GOVERNMENT AND LABOR AS APPLICABLE

ANY NECESSARY COMBINATION

GOVERNMENT (INFORMATION ONLY)

* NOT WITHIN DIRECT SCOPE OF SECTION 1010 OF MODEL CITIES ACT BUT VITAL TO URBAN EXCELLENCE AND/OR NECESSARY TO IMPLEMENT 1010 AND SHOULD BE PART OF PARALLEL PROGRAM

** MARKET OPPORTUNITY FOR PRIVATE ENTERPRISE

Appendix B

Extracts from Building Research Advisory Board's Report,
*Historical Evaluation of Industrialized Housing and
Building Systems*

OBJECTIVES

Early in 1968 the Building Research Advisory Board, with support provided
by a grant from the Ford Foundation, appointed a Special Advisory Committee to investigate and report on the state of the art of housing industrialization in America. Specifically, the objectives established were as follows:

1. To determine, to the extent possible, the types of and production
magnitude involved in componentized and preassembled structures used
primarily for single- and multifamily housing since World War II;

2. To collect and synthesize data from a representative sample of programs
involving such structures to determine the extent of success or failure, the
reasons for success or failure, and what factors might have assisted in further-
ing success or preventing failure; and

3. To provide conclusions about the feasibility and limitations of industrialized construction.

SCOPE

The major investigative effort was concentrated on single- and multifamily
housing. Nonresidential systems were studied only in the context of their
potential application to housing.

The program initially was directed toward the technical aspects of industrialized systems, but it was quickly determined that what appeared to be a
peripheral factor—e.g., the socioeconomic climate—was, in fact, intimately

related to the success or failure of many attempts at industrialized construction. Accordingly, investigation of such other factors became part of the study.

To give expression to the broader concept of housing industrialization accepted for purposes of its study, the committee developed the following definition:

The total process of producing housing in a viable community including the application and implementation of significant advances in production methods, tools, equipment, financing, distribution, land management, organization, and management techniques constitutes industrialization in housing and building. The terms "mass production," "assembly line manufacture," and "prefabrication" are specific aspects of industrialization.

CONCLUSIONS*

1. Industrialization in housing has been progressing over the years, beginning with small elements, and advancing in evolutionary stages to even larger and more sophisticated components.

Industrialization in housing has been evolutionary, beginning with small elements, and advancing in progressive stages to ever larger and more sophisticated components. This evolution developed from individual pieces to prehung doors, and from sectionalized wall panels to sectionalized rooms and mobile homes. These products and components are, or may be, manufactured by mass-production methods in factories. Also evolutionary in nature has been the continued and growing utilization of the technique of on-site division of labor in a planned pattern of assembly and joining operations.

2. Most industrialization attempts have dealt with the building envelope, which represents only about one-sixth of the total cost.

Attempts to industrialize the building envelope have not significantly reduced total costs. Study results revealed that the envelope accounts for about one-sixth of the total price paid by the buyer for housing. Opportunities for significant cost savings are more likely in a combination of factors that represent the other five-sixths of the total cost—such as land, core, and financing. Any effort to reduce costs must consider the total process of housing, not just one particular aspect.

Industrialization of certain larger components, such as sectionalized rooms,

*Extracts from the discussions upon which the conclusions and recommendations are based follow each conclusion.

has resulted in actual manufacturing economy, but these savings have some-times been canceled due to transportation and distribution costs that exceeded budgeted amounts. Related to the localized market problem (see conclusion No. 3), the volume of potential business in transporting factory-made sections has not been great enough to interest transportation companies in developing specialized units for economically hauling housing components, as has been done for high-volume items such as coal and automobiles.

On-site industrialization has produced some savings in erection of the envelope and, even more significantly, in the over-all costs due to optimum scheduling and control of the process. Those interviewed did not, however, believe that there were any significant breakthroughs on the horizon that will substantially reduce single-family housing costs through industrialized methods of on-site construction.

As for prefabrication of houses, most attempts (excluding mobile homes) have failed to reduce housing construction costs significantly, although some savings on actual erection time have been noted, as have marginal operating advantages in areas of labor and material shortages. Under prevailing market conditions, the large amount of capital required for facilities, inventories, accounts receivable, and the added costs of transportation of prefabricated units from factory to job site have caused factory-prefabricated housing units to cost no less than those conventionally built. Moreover, the expected growth of the prefabricated home industry has not occurred because of increased cost competition that has resulted from refinements in on-site fabrication. By moving toward subcontracting of all the elements of the house and toward increased use of on-site assembly methods, the conventional builder has attained closer control and lower costs. For example, he can replace a subcontractor who has not met time and cost goals, and find a more effective performer. In contrast, the builder who is tied to a prefabricator's system cannot take such corrective action so readily or so promptly.

3. Industrialization, as associated with large-scale mass production of standardized housing units, has been limited in scope because housing markets in the United States are numerous, small, discretionary, cyclic, and local in nature.

Markets for housing in the United States have been fragmented and are becoming progressively more numerous, discretionary, cyclic, and local in nature, making large-scale mass production of standardized housing units questionable. The financial and corporate community, observing this segmentation of the market, has seemingly concluded that evolutionary advances in industrialization are the accepted way of improvement in the construction field and has not furnished capital for the large-scale investment in plant and equipment that would be required for true mass production.

This is no single market for housing analogous to that for the multimillion sales of a relatively few standardized models of cars. The markets for housing are many, small, and cyclic, and there appears to be a limit to market size in any given locale, at any one time, for any particular type of single-family house, within a particular price range.

4. The technical knowledge needed to effectively industrialize the housing industry and thus achieve large-scale mass production exists now.

The technical knowledge needed to effectively industrialize housing and achieve large-scale mass production exists now, or can be readily supplied when a market is clearly identified. The constraints imposed by social, political, and economic factors have been more important than lack of technology.

The housing industry has had access to the technological process that has taken place in almost every kind of manufacturing activity. That it has had (and has now) the technical knowledge to arrive at highly rationalized and sophisticated systems of house and house component manufacture is on record. The assembly line for the Lustron Home, moving by automation over eight miles of conveyor—but with the many parts hand-loaded onto a specially designed trailer for movement to the construction site and interim storage there—was an early attempt. Another try at assembly-line manfacture was the Alsides Home, produced with even greater precision and speed, but with far fewer parts. The open-air factory set up for the manufacture of the concrete "boxes" which comprised complete rooms, and which were crane-hoisted into position to build a 21-story hotel in San Antonio in less than 9 months from plan inception, was an ingenious construction system incorporating some of the very latest advances in concrete forming, casting, and curing. The one-piece (literally) bathrooms and kitchens of molded fiberglass for Montreal's Habitat '67 represented good technical design and precision manufacture. The assembly operations that turn out today's mobile homes and the technology that may make it possible to take these mobile homes and "plug" them into slots in a structure built around a utility core for high-density housing assuredly represent technological ingenuity. But technical knowledge and technology have not been sufficient to ensure success of an industrialized system of housing manufacturers. Other factors, mostly nontechnical, have been more important determinants of the success or failure of systems and have served as constraints to even greater application of technical knowledge. As these constraints (political, regulatory, and institutional inflexibility; and lack of capitalization) change, and as labor shortages become even more critical, applications of available technology are likely to accelerate.

5. *Nontechnical variables, such as codes, zoning, taxation, financing, and labor have acted as constraints to the most effective application of industrialization to housing and building.*

Many of the variables of the marketplace have acted as constraints to the greater application of industrialization to the building of houses in a viable community.

The period required for the introduction and acceptance of new concepts in industrialization of housing has tended to be long—approximately seven to ten years. The traditional tastes of most home buyers play a significant role in this time lag. For example, most successful ventures in the prefabrication of houses have utilized traditional materials in traditional designs; in contrast, the most conspicuous failures used nontraditional materials in semitraditional or severely contemporary designs. Financial backers have often resisted technical innovations because of doubts concerning long-term performance, fear of potential hidden costs, and concern for consumer acceptance. A lack of confidence in accelerated pilot tests and the nonavailability of full-scale repetitive field tests have also been factors. Thus, instead of innovating, many entrepreneurs—homebuilders or manufacturers—have developed improved models of existing products in order to reduce the resistance of home buyers or financial backers and to minimize the amount of retraining required for all concerned in marketing and applying the product. The risks, when innovations are introduced, too often are thrust on a third party, usually the subcontractor, who is least able to stand a financial loss and who also has the least to gain. This third party, however, may be the key to the success or failure of the innovation. Any lack of experience or resistance to change may cancel out the potential advantages of innovation. Manufacturers have recently recognized this problem and have been providing subcontractors with much better direction and technical assistance and have been willing to provide financial support as required. Despite these constraints, as earlier noted, incremental changes, including many new products, have been successfully introduced.

Codes per se were not found to be the direct reason for failures of the past industrialized systems, although they did constrain freedom of choice in technology and have limited the market. Field interviews revealed that entrepreneurs either learned to "live" with codes as they existed or they avoided marketing areas with restrictive codes. Codes have traditionally been locally promulgated and administered. They have been viewed primarily as a means to ensure protection of the purchaser but have often been used for different purposes, such as controlling the type of housing to be erected. The field study clearly revealed the lack of uniformity of codes. It was felt that this lack of uniformity required an entrepreneur to meet the highest requirement in his chosen marketing area at additional costs or to attempt to change the codes to accommodate his material, product, or method. Although there were often justifications for local variations, such as geographical or climatic conditions, most interviewers felt that the variations were too large to be justified on this basis alone.

Another constraint to industrialization concerns the home-buyer's desire for options and for individuality. In all his purchasing, he is accustomed to and demands a broad variety of choices. Industrialized single-family housing systems have, for the most part, been standardized in an unsophisticated manner and the consequent restrictions on design and flexibility have caused them to fall short of satisfying localized preferences.

Literature search and field interviews indicate that labor practices and variations in factory and field labor rates have acted both as a constraint on development of industrialized building systems and as a stimulant to it. The reluctance of field craftsmen to install factory-assembled components, especially when assembled outside their jurisdictions, has operated as a constraint. On the other hand, the wage-scale differences, usually lower rates for factory workers, have acted as a stimulant to development of factory-produced building components and systems.

With shortages of craftsmen now becoming increasingly more severe, particularly in trades such as carpentry, brick masonry, cement masonry, plumbers, and electricians; and with ever-higher wages, it seems obvious that the job of producing 2.5 million homes a year, as called for by the President, will continue to stimulate utilization of more factory-produced components and less on-site fabrication.

6. *The ability of management to deal effectively with the total process, from conception to occupancy within a viable community, has been a major factor in the success or failure of endeavors to industrialize housing and building.*

Lack of proper management control, particularly in the area of finance and marketing, has contributed to many project failures. Two types of failure have occurred: the first, when the factory-fabricated-house producer had higher costs than those prevailing in the competitive market; the second, when he far underestimated the lead time required for the product to gain market acceptance, so that facility investment costs and overheads mounted markedly before there was any return. In the development of new towns and new subdivisions, the inability to sequence operations correctly, with investment for sewers, streets, and the like being too far ahead of current sales, instead of in step with them, adversely affected cash flow and caused other projects to fail.

Even when single-family house construction and sales have been the principle concern, most entrepreneurs have recognized that volume production required a large volume of purchasers. But some have failed to recognize that an equally important part of this situation is the timely development of an equivalent number of lots (including utilities and other public facilities) to serve as sites for the product of their factories. Although the importance of management was recognized during earlier attempts at setting up completely industrialized housing systems, the need often was interpreted somewhat narrowly. For example, "mass production" management specialists sometimes were recruited from other industries. They thought chiefly in terms of solving factory production problems and thus did not recognize the importance of marketing, including distribution, financing, and erection. This contributed to their lack of success.

RECOMMENDATIONS

1. *Management of Total Process*   The need for increased skills and knowledge in administering a broader, total approach to building in a viable community provides reason to encourage the building industry to establish programs aimed at increasing the competence of management at all levels.

2. *Constraints*   A major effort should be made to identify and analyze critically those constraints considered handicaps to the development of industrialization in housing and to its potential economies of scale, and to evolve programs for minimizing those constraints, including codes, zoning, and taxation.

If, for example, industry is to devise meaningful approaches to using industrialized techniques to supply low-cost housing, the type and mix of housing required, where it is needed, and under what conditions must be determined.

3. *Cost Analysis*   Realistic assessments of unit costs of proposed industrialized housing systems would do much to avoid failures and premature investments in unworthy proposals. Public costs for both single-family housing and multifamily housing should be included in such assessments. To this end, entrepreneurs seeking public support should be required to make and submit complete cost–benefit analyses of their proposals; including not only near-term costs (today the sole requirement) but long-term costs as well, and also such costs that are related to the introduction and proving-out of new con-

cepts. These total costs should then be a major factor in any decision to support the program.

Industrialized systems of multifamily high-rise housing are most advanced in both western and eastern Europe. These systems should be studied in detail to ascertain whether they offer potential for real economies in the United States market climate. Particular attention should be given to obtaining on-site data and information, utilizing teams of competent personnel familiar with United States operations. In fact, a control cost-analysis experiment should be conducted in the United States at the same time to ensure sound correlation of information.

Since the greater potential for reducing costs of low-income family housing lies in land, core, financing, and large-scale project management, the attention of government and industry should be concentrated in these areas.

Although it was found that raw land costs generally were lower in the suburbs than in urban areas, the development of suburban land requires additional expenditures for many public services, e.g., police and fire protection, streets, sidewalks, schools, and parks, which were not known. Thus, the true cost of suburban land actually might be higher than land in the cities, where such public facilities already exist, at least in part. Therefore, it is recommended that a study be made to set criteria for determining public costs and, thus, true costs of land.

4. *Flexibility to Meet the Needs* The desirability of free interchange of housing and building components seems undeniable in terms of both economy of time and material and of conservation of resources. To this end, the development of open systems and compatible closed systems of industrialized housing should be encouraged, i.e., those systems in which there is extensive modularization of all components and a system for interlocking the products of different systems.

So that competent manufacturers or contractors will be afforded incentives to participate in rehabilitation programs on a continuing basis, reasonable criteria should be developed in rehabilitation of substandard housing.

Special situations such as developing areas, inner-city renewal, rehabilitation, and new community developments demand greater flexibility of regulatory authority. This suggests the need for a study to determine the possibility of adjusting codes, zoning, and standards to meet these special needs.

The decision as to whether to rehabilitate, renew, or undertake new construction of dilapidated communities must be based on sound criteria. To this end, a study should be made to establish such criteria.

5. *Standards and Tests* Through the performance approach, technological needs should be determined as a basis for setting standards for each desired level of construction quality. Techniques and test procedures then should be

developed with which to judge whether innovations will comply with the standards.

6. *Government Stimulus* Meeting a national goal of 2.5 million new housing units a year, as called for by the President in 1968, suggests the magnitude of effort that has been characteristic of certain other programs such as space exploration, development of atomic energy for peaceful uses, and health. To this end, it is suggested that government establish a definitive priority for housing and urban development; and then give the problems of planners and producers the attention needed for more effective access to and utilization of the nation's resources. Doing this will encourage further and more rapid development of effective industrialized housing systems and housing production.

7. *Land Development* Individual house utility and service systems may be the means of freeing the attachment of the house to the land, making it more responsive to the need for mobility and to changing patterns of land use. To this end, it is suggested that an examination into the entire complex problem of over-all utility and service systems be made with the goal of determining the advantages and disadvantages of both centralized and decentralized systems.

Appendix C

Growth of Local Government Financing

GROWTH OF LOCAL GOVERNMENT FINANCING IN BILLIONS OF DOLLARS

	1902[a]	1929[b]	1948[b]	1956[b]	1966
Expenditures (dollars)	1.0	6.4	11.7	25.0	56.5
Revenue from local sources[c] (dollars)	0.9	5.5	8.2	16.6	35.5
Revenue/expenditures (percent)	90.0	85.9	70.1	66.4	62.8
Nonfarm disposable income[b] (dollars)	14.5	75.8	179.2	281.8	490.0
Revenue/nonfarm disposable income (percent)	6.2	7.3	4.6	5.9	7.2
Expenditures/nonfarm disposable income (percent)	6.9	8.4	6.5	8.9	11.5
Property tax (dollars)	0.6	4.3	5.9	11.3	24.3
Property tax/nonfarm disposable income (percent)	4.1	5.7	3.3	4.0	5.0

[a]Fiscal data taken from Industrial Conference Board, October 1966, table on page 22. Income data from NPA.

[b]Personal income data from National Income & Products Accounts, 1929–1965, Tables 1.7, 1.11, 2.1.
Some estimation necessary to eliminate farm disposable income.

[c]Includes revenues from fees, contributions for Social Security, government enterprises, etc.

Appendix D

A Summary Report of the Recommendations of the
Committee on Social and Behavioral Urban Research and
the Committee on Urban Technology

INTRODUCTION

The Committee on Social and Behavioral Urban Research and the Committee
on Urban Technology were composed with different primary emphases and
different skills. The membership of COSBUR was drawn predominantly from
the social sciences and largely from universities, while CUT was composed
primarily of engineers drawn from industry and universities.

The two committees shared a commitment to the view that the resolution
of current and future urban problems is fundamental to the life of the nation,
and that the research and development contribution to successful management of these problems will place an enormous demand on the engineering,
technical, and scientific resources of the nation.

The initial meeting of the two committees was in part a joint session during
which the committees were briefed by representatives from the Department
of Housing and Urban Development on the current status of the Department's
research and development program. Prior to the transmittal of the committees' interim reports to the Department, an executive group, composed of the
chairmen and two members from each committee, met and reviewed the
activities of the two committees and agreed on a common outline for interim
reports of the committees. Except for the initial and executive committee
meetings and periodic briefings by staff on the accomplishments and directions of the parallel effort, the two committees worked separately and independently. Agreement in the recommendations of the two committees is particularly significant in that they were arrived at independently. In view of the
independence of the separate committees, it may be assumed that a high degree of priority should be given to those recommendations on which the com-

mittees agree. The emphasis in this summary coordinated report, therefore, is on those recommendations.

In addition to agreement between the two committees on several recommendations, they also reached somewhat different but, nonetheless, complementary conclusions with respect to some matters, as a consequence of having taken different approaches to them. In these instances, differences should be viewed as mutually additive or reinforcing. It should be added that there were no fundamental differences in the advice given by the two committees to the Department of Housing and Urban Development, except perhaps as these may arise from the underlying conceptual frameworks that served to guide the committees' work.

Finally, with respect to the summary report of the separate recommendations of the two committees which follows, the fact that certain particular recommendations appear among those of one but not of both of the committees' reports does not mean that they are of any less importance to the Department of Housing and Urban Development. Given the independence of the committees' efforts and the diversity of perspective and areas of competence represented in their memberships, it would be surprising, indeed, if all recommendations emerged simultaneously from the efforts of both committees. The recommendations of the two committees and the reasoning and findings on which they are based are reported in detail, of course, in the separate reports of the two groups.

This summary report of the recommendations on strategies for urban research and development responds to a request from the Department of Housing and Urban Development. It is a summation of the recommendations developed independently by the Committee on Social and Behavioral Urban Research and the Committee on Urban Technology since the organizing meeting of those committees on December 12, 1967. More complete recommendations, together with discussions on which they are based, are to be found in the separate reports of the two committees.

STRATEGIES FOR PLANNING RESEARCH

Both committees stress a strategic approach to research and development, which confirms the fact that hardware and software must be considered and planned for together and that they are not mutually exclusive investment alternatives. Both committees argue for the advantages of a multidisciplinary approach to urban problems and concur in the recommendation that first priority in developing the Department's research and development program should be given to mobilizing and creating new social and behavioral science research and application capabilities. The committees agree further that the buildup of software requirements should complement rather than substitute for investments in technological research and development. The Committee on Urban Technology finds that

Both physical technology and social technology must be brought together in evaluating and implementing solutions to urban problems. . . . Accordingly, the development of the "social engineer" through the efforts of the universities, municipal governments, and the Department of Housing and Urban Development should have the highest priority. This type of capability is essential to define the needs and thus provide the performance objectives to be satisfied by evaluation of the wealth of available physical technology.

From a different perspective, the Committee on Social and Behavioral Urban Research arrived at the same conclusion:

This country, as well as other societies, is still being penalized because the human dimensions of the urban process are so poorly understood. In the absence of a purposeful and concerted effort to remedy this situation and to anticipate both the future problems and opportunities that urban America may face, it will continue to be penalized. For such an effort, the social and behavioral sciences are both relevant and useful, if not critical. They make possible the shift from an emphasis on "bricks and mortar" questions in urban research and development to a systematic emphasis on questions that, when answers are forthcoming, will illuminate processes of social change, provide information about human consequences of urban problems, and point to new options for social action.

In setting forth additional priorities in a strategic approach to urban research and development, both committees give heavy weight to the need for program evaluation research. This conclusion was approached by the committees in different ways that should be made explicit. The Committee on Urban Technology, in giving primary emphasis to assessing the value of implementing available technology, viewed each implementation as an operational experiment designed expressly for the purpose of observation and analysis as to its contribution to urban improvement. The realization of the physical design and cost estimates of these experiments should in each instance be evaluated. Project evaluation in this sense is a short-term effort. However, the evaluation of the social and behavioral consequences of both technological and social projects and programs is agreed by the committees to be a continuous and long-term activity. The Committee on Social and Behavioral Urban Research assumes that policies and programs must be under constant scrutiny if they are to achieve their intended results and, therefore, recommends that program evaluation research be given high priority in the allocation of the Department's research and development resources.

Another element in choosing among priorities in a strategic approach to urban research and development is, of course, the allocation of resources between short-term and long-range projects. The two committees agree on the value and necessity of relatively short-term investments, but they also agree that a significant proportion of research and development funds should be invested in research and development activities that might be expected to yield contributions in a long-term period. The Committee on Urban Technology recommends that 50 to 60 percent of the Department's research and development resources should be put into projects for early implementation, and 30 to 40 percent should be allocated for long-range projects. The Committee on Social and Behavioral Urban Research agrees on the merit of short-term research and development projects, particularly as they relate to the implementation of new technology. The committees agree that proof on a limited scale is an essential step before widespread applications are undertaken in a large number of cities or unduly large sums committed to short-term projects. If scientific and technological knowledge and inquiry are to serve the society well, they must be used in part to inhibit action on attractive but misconceived courses, as well as to create new options for action.

Both committees concluded that, while the buildup of research and development capabilities should receive first-order priority, the guiding principle for setting priorities should be that the development of capabilities, manpower and funding be kept carefully in phase. Thus, allocations of money should neither exceed nor fall short of qualified manpower and its capabilities for implementing the projects to which the money is allocated. On the other hand, sufficient funds should be allocated to support the manpower and capabilities assigned. An important preliminary to the achievement of the proper balance is an accurate survey of the qualified manpower that is available.

Both committees recommend that a coordinated development of available and potential resources should proceed at a level of magnitude that would double the Department's research and development effort each year for three to five years as an initial step. Beyond this, the Committee on Urban Technology recommends a contingency plan of accelerated activities to be undertaken coincident with the conclusion of United States participation in the Vietnam war. This plan would depend on the capability that has been achieved at the time the accelerated allocation of resources would be made available and could involve enhancement of research, of development, or of application efforts. The Committee on Urban Technology is in agreement with the Committee on Social and Behavioral Urban Research on the point that, whatever funds are available, research and development priorities determined primarily by a sense of urgency to show results must be complemented by the need to develop programs and resources that will contribute to improving the quality of urban life over the years to come.

In the citation and discussion of essential recommendations that follow, an attempt is made to correlate in summary form the recommendations of the two committees, so as to illuminate the essential perspectives and significance of the full reports of the committees.

In considering the basic strategy for developing the Department's research and development program, the Committee on Urban Technology concludes that

While there are significant research opportunities that will bring forward new technology that will contribute to urban improvement, the primary opportunity resides in the effective application of available technology to the most urgent urban development problems. . . . Particular emphasis must be given to efforts by the applied social scientists that will define these needs and requirements and thus guide the technological efforts.

Examples of possible applications of available technology are improvements in factory-produced low-cost housing; the use of sophisticated systems for the provision of such utilities as water, energy, communication, chilled water for air conditioning, and waste disposal; and more efficient planning for land use.

With respect to the basic approach to be adopted in formulating research and development policies and programs, the Committee on Social and Behavioral Urban Research recommends that the Department of Housing and Urban Development

. . . establish R&D program priorities in a manner consistent with the principle that the growth of extramural R&D expenditures be kept in phase with the mobilization of existing and potential R&D capabilities, the development of manpower, and the creation of new capabilities; begin immediately on the tasks of strengthening present R&D capabilities and creating new ones in the social and behavioral sciences. . . .

This is, to begin with, a matter of determining the best resources for various tasks, that is, university, industry, nonprofit, municipal government, inhouse. The effectiveness of the extramural network will depend on inhouse insights and capabilities, permitting the most efficient use of the resources of the network in planning, programming, and execution of research and other tasks. Accordingly, the Committee on Social and Behavioral Urban Research recommends that the Department of Housing and Urban Development

. . . allocate its R&D budget so that (1) a substantial share is earmarked for the orderly development of a network of extramural research and development capabilities, including the required supplies of scientific and professional manpower; (2) a significant portion is devoted to program evaluation activities; and (3) adequate provision is made to support short-run research centering on the implications of the results of efforts to measure the effects of the urban program for policy intentions.

RESEARCH AND DEVELOPMENT CAPABILITIES

Research and development activities must be related to the manpower and institutional resources available for conducting them. This requires that a program for investment in R&D be accompanied by programs designed to (1) assure access to and effective use of available R&D capabilities; (2) enhance existing manpower and institutional resources; and (3) help bring into being and assist in the growth of new R&D institutions as required. In the absence of planned efforts along these lines, there is no assurance that investments in R&D will produce results useful for the entire range of decision-making involved in planning, implementing, evaluating, and reformulating or modifying policies and programs.

The two committees agree that the Department's present policy of having most of its research and development conducted extramurally through contracts and grants is sound. The network of related extramural research and development capabilities needed by the Department of Housing and Urban Development can be constructed in part by mobilizing existing research capabilities, so as to bring them more effectively to bear on issues of social policy. In addition to utilizing available research capabilities, the committees agree that the Department must also create new institutional capabilities to achieve those mission-oriented research objectives for which existing resources are likely to be unresponsive or unsuitable. Further, both committees stress the critical importance of the Department's inhouse research and development capability for the establishment of goals, program planning, project management, and evaluation. These specific recommendations of the two committees for developing a coherent network of relevant research and development activities are aimed at meeting the Department's research and development needs by university, industrial, nonprofit, municipal government, inhouse, and other capabilities.

With respect to mobilizing existing university research and development capabilities the Committee on Social and Behavioral Urban Research recommends that the Department of Housing and Urban Development support

• basic research in the behavioral and social sciences, as well as in the natural sciences, to contribute to the growth of knowledge and its application to the problems of the city;

• a small number of university urban institutes or centers, on a continuing basis, selected on the basis of staff competence and diversity of interest and location, and expand the number of such institutes or centers as funds become available;

• unsolicited as well as solicited proposals that meet the criteria of merit and quality by grant and contract; and

• university educational training programs related to urban needs by providing funds for curriculum revision, facilities, and predoctoral and postdoctoral fellowships.

To encourage universities to strengthen and redirect their capabilities and to apply their talents to the requirements for training, research, and community participation in urban affairs, the Committee on Urban Technology recommends to the Department of Housing and Urban Development that

An inventory should be taken of the capabilities that now exist or that might be developed in the universities. This should then be compared with a projection of requirements for professional manpower to determine a basis for further fellowship support.... Universities should be encouraged to join their efforts with local governments and industry to develop viable programs of education seeking to improve the capability of those involved in urban management.

One of the quickest ways to fill the gap between the need and the supply of professional manpower is to embark on a program of mid-career updating of selected persons who have a potential for carrying greater responsibility and who are now employed in urban management. This might take the form of a three-month study of modern urban science and technology (MUST) with lecturers from universities, government, urban institutes, and industry. The course should not attempt to make each manager an expert in a narrow discipline, but rather to orient each toward an increased understanding of relationships, interfaces, and the application of modern tools for managing urban affairs.

With respect to utilization of existing nonacademic private research and development capabilities, the Committee on Social and Behavioral Urban Research recommends that the Department of Housing and Urban Development

... systematically survey existing private profit and nonprofit research and development organizations and consulting firms to assess their resources for undertaking urban-related R&D and to set standards of expected performance.

In order to take advantage of the talent and managerial experience of industry, the Committee on Urban Technology recommends to the Department of Housing and Urban Development that

... [it] establish a seminar and continuing dialogue with industrial leaders to explore in depth the terms and conditions industry would need in specific community situations to reduce the risks of participation to acceptable levels. This is necessary because, in general, two main factors will govern industrial participation: the risk and the market, that is, the potential volume of activity. One way of overcoming the risk factor is to have private enterprise act as an agent for a government agency. Such an arrangement enables private industry to contribute its management experience and technical capability with minimum risk to the stockholder.

In order to create coherent applied research and development capabilities, the Committee on Social and Behavioral Urban Research recommends that the Department of Housing and Urban Development

. . . undertake the planning activities required to bring six additional urban institutes into being, including exploration of the opportunities to create such institutes by modifying or expanding research centers now associated with other federal agencies, private organizations, or universities.

The Committee believes that the urban institutes should have a continuing functional relationship with the Department of Housing and Urban Development but that the institutes themselves should work out strategies for research and define responsibilities for detailed operations. The Department and the institutes should work out effective balances of problem-solving and training functions, as particular areas and programs require.

With respect to the use of the Urban Institute as a research and development resource, the Committee on Urban Technology observes that the newly created Urban Institute

. . . could be a source of creative contributions; it could test hypotheses; it could evaluate alternatives; and it could compare evaluations made by other groups.

The Department's funding should emphasize this kind of contribution to the departmental mission. The Department's dependence on the Institute will require some continuity of funding at a level sufficient to maintain a healthy, productive, and efficient work force in the Institute devoted to the Department's requirements. This is often referred to as a staff of "critical size."

To create research and development capabilities in state and local governments, the Committee on Social and Behavioral Urban Research recommends that the Department of Housing and Urban Development

- experiment with the form, location, and funding of Municipal Development Centers (MDC's) to discover the most effective means for strengthening research capabilities in municipal governments;
- secure authorization for programs designed to expand the supplies of scientific, professional, and related manpower for service with local governments in connection with urban affairs; and
- examine the means by which urban R&D capabilities can be provided for state governments.

The experiment with establishment of MDC's should be conducted so as to be consistent with the development of external research and development capabilities, that is, to achieve as wide a variety of forms, competencies, and "end-products" as possible from the investment of scarce resources. Therefore, the Department of Housing and Urban Development should

. . . increase the number of MDC's each successive year over the next three years to about 25, so as to provide an experimental base for determining whether the MDC's should be made operational on a national scale. . . .

The principal aim of the MDC program is to link a research and development capability to competent municipal administration. The Committee on Social and Behavioral Urban Research recommends that the Department of Housing and Urban Development, while constantly reviewing its original six pilot efforts, increase the number of MDC's each year over the next three years to provide an experimental base to determine whether they should be made operational on a national scale. An experimental base of between 20 and 30 centers would be sufficient to provide the information and experience required for such a decision. The Committee recommends that the Department

. . . evaluate the success of the MDC experiment as an attempt to (1) provide for mutually profitable relations between researchers and local decision-makers, (2) attract professional manpower into local government, (3) produce new and needed skills, (4) contribute to the information requirements for sound policy judgment at all levels of government, and . . . exercise sufficient control over the MDC's to assure a reasonable body of comparable data for use by local, state, and national research bodies. . . .

In order to broaden the viewpoint and upgrade the professional competence in state and city operating organizations, the Committee on Urban Technology recommends to the Department of Housing and Urban Development that

. . . consideration should be given to the possibility of collaborating with existing organizations concerned with developing a professional city management.

Opportunities to work with academic institutions and industry should be welcomed by city administrators. One way of relating to university capability might be to create openings for young faculty members or graduate students to spend a year or more as city employees, with freedom to maintain close and formal relations with the urban research facilities of their home institutions. Such a cooperative urban fellowship program could become a means for recruiting and developing applied social scientists.

With respect to developing the Department's intramural research and development capabilities, the Committee on Social and Behavioral Urban Research recommends that the Department of Housing and Urban Development

. . . increase its intramural multidisciplinary R&D staff to between 75 and 100 professionals over the next five years and draw personnel from outside as well as from within the social and behavioral sciences; offer salaries and working conditions that will attract able and experienced personnel from the academic and industrial worlds, making provision for a large proportion of higher grades and a disproportionately large number of "supergrades."

It should be anticipated that the Department of Housing and Urban Development will encourage and facilitate the mobility of research specialists among the urban institutes, municipal development centers, universities, industry, and the Department's inhouse staff. Fellowship programs should attract university researchers for short periods of service with the Department. The committees join in recommending that the Department of Housing and Urban Development

. . . complement its inhouse capabilities with independent advisory bodies on R&D policies and programs.

The Department will want to continue to use consultants on technical problems and policy issues to complement its own staff resources. Whether the Department's most sanguine budget hopes are realized or frustrated, it will be in better position to set priorities and allocate resources for research and development if it can secure informed and tough-minded advice from external sources on both an *ad hoc* and a continuing basis.

In order to enhance the research and development staff capabilities within the Department, the Committee on Urban Technology recommends to the Department of Housing and Urban Development that

. . . the magnitude and importance of the urban problems warrant applying substantially more of the Department's staff to its urban research and development mission, suggesting an annual doubling of the research and development effort each year for at least three years;

the Department should develop a staff project management structure for monitoring, guidance, and correlation of projects developed within the Department but carried out elsewhere under contract.

Such a structure is necessary as long as the Department does not possess an inhouse research capability. Many projects should be carried out by private research agencies and the private entrepreneurial community with experience in practical matters of urban development. Some will be appropriate for urban institutes and in universities, however, and invitations to respond to such proposals should continue to go to those institutions that have specific capabilities in the relevant areas of technology and applied science, and that have unique opportunity to work with local governments. The Committee on Urban Technology recommends that the Department of Housing and Urban Development

. . . make provisions for the discretionary use of some portion of contracted funds, develop mechanisms to process unsolicited proposals, and support state and local research and development programs through contract.

POLICY ANALYSIS AND PROGRAM EVALUATION

The two committees agree on the importance of goal analysis and program evaluation for making research and development efforts relevant for the formulation of departmental policies and programs. With respect to research and development contributions to policy analysis and program evaluation, the Committee on Social and Behavioral Urban Research recommends that the Department of Housing and Urban Development

- devote a major and continuing inhouse effort to the translation of statutory statements of goals into operational terms, so that the relationships assumed to lie between goals and the instrumentalities for realizing them are made explicit and amenable to research;
- continue to have the Director of the Office of Urban Technology and Research report directly to the highest levels within the Department;
- invest a significant proportion of its R&D budget in evaluation research on all operating programs; and
- conduct evaluation research designed to assess both the intended and the unanticipated effects of programs on a continuing basis, so that the results will contribute fully to the reformulation and modification of policies and programs.

The Committee on Urban Technology believes that the establishment of goals for the departmental mission is of the greatest immediate importance and that the application of technology to the spectrum of community problems should be continuously evaluated, and, therefore, concludes that

. . . a structure for the continuous evaluation of the results of urban technology programs be developed; approximately 5 to 10 percent of the program funds should be devoted to evaluation. More may be needed to guide and support program planning.

The development of criteria for evaluation and the scheduling of periodic evaluations should be required elements in all project work statements. Such an approach should assure maximum learning from each project; identify technology, plans, and programs that deserve dissemination; avoid repetition of less fruitful paths; guide formulation of new projects; and provide experience information to assist in the selection among both solicited and unsolicited project proposals.

RESEARCH AND DEVELOPMENT PROGRAMS

Contemporary attitudes toward intended social change and techniques for effecting them make the role of information increasingly important in both planning and implementing action decisions. A powerful tool in the national effort for urban reform and reconstruction would be the capacity for the systematic collection, storage, processing, and selective dissemination of data relevant to urban needs and the functioning of urban programs. The two committees agree that the Department of Housing and Urban Development is in a position to assume the key role in the development of information requirements, resources, and systems, and thus to contribute to the creation of operationally effective urban information systems.

With respect to research and development related to developing urban information systems, the Committee on Social and Behavioral Urban Research recommends that the Department of Housing and Urban Development

- organize its data, information, and measurement activities under an Office of Information Management;
- associate itself with several major attempts to develop, test, and evaluate specific information systems, but refrain from investing sizable resources in the development of large-scale urban information systems until there is a better understanding of how they can best be introduced and constructed; and.
- devote a special effort to systematic investigation of the kinds of urban intelligence systems that would complement the growth of urban information systems.

The Department is in a position to assume the key role in the development of urban information systems and thus contribute to the creation of a national urban information system. Its activities in the information field, therefore, should, to the extent now possible, be based on an overall model of what a complete information system to meet national urban needs would be like. The Committee on Urban Technology confirmed the recommendations of the Committee on Social and Behavioral Urban Research in its report.

With respect to planning activities and urban information needs, the Committee on Social and Behavioral Urban Research recommends that the Department of Housing and Urban Development

. . . provide immediate support for research that will provide two kinds of information requirements: (1) demographic studies, for which the significant variables and the methods for data gathering and analysis are immediately available and the results of which are known to be relevant, and (2) studies of the conditions of variations in neighborhood cohesion, for which the variables and significant measures have yet to be developed but which can be stipulated to have major significance and long-run relevance.

With respect to urban research and development planning and urban information needs, the Committee on Urban Technology recommends to the Department of Housing and Urban Development that

. . . the immediate planning efforts of the Department should include program planning among its major objectives. This will require: (1) examination of historical trends, (2) establishment of an information system, (3) research and analysis of the urban environment for opportunities and constraints, and (4) synthesis and evaluation of alternative courses of action.

The magnitude and expanding nature of these tasks warrant a substantial increase in the Department's capabilities as competent personnel become available. In addition to personnel with a high level of competence in the sociological area, the Department will require persons who are competent in the development and operation of a logical systems analysis structure, and persons who are knowledgeable in both the availability and the application of technology in synthesizing feasible alternative solutions to urban problems as well as evaluating the worth of alternative solutions. Accordingly, the Committee on Urban Technology recommends that

. . . the Department should assume the leadership in establishing a mechanism to correlate the mission responsibilities of all the federal agencies concerned with various aspects of urban research and development planning. In addition to representation from the federal agencies, there should be representation of the viewpoints of industry, universities, and special institutions.

With respect to the promise of "the systems approach" for coping with urban problems or for designing research and development programs, the Committee on Social and Behavioral Urban Research recommends that the Department of Housing and Urban Development

. . . support multidisciplinary research to identify the systems parameters and interacting properties of urban units, investing only modestly in the immediate future in computer-aided simulations of the urban environment.

The Committee on Urban Technology recommends that

. . . the task of urban development cannot be undertaken without consideration of and planning for the interrelationship of the whole community, including both the suburbs and the urban areas.

With regard to specific substantive research and development topics that should be supported by the Department of Housing and Urban Development, the differences in the recommendations of the two committees reflect differences in their areas of competence, but the results of these independent efforts are not in opposition. Indeed, the committees with to reemphasize the virtue and necessity of viewing technological and social and behavioral science research and development requirements as inseparable in a strategic approach to improving the quality of urban life.

With respect to overcoming obstacles to implementing present policies and finding new program instruments, the Committee on Social and Behavioral Urban Research recommends that the Department of Housing and Urban Development support specific research projects in the following areas:

• local governance, as, for example, (1) studies of the ways different types of governments function in different social environments, and (2) the advisability of transferring functions from one to another form of government;

• fiscal policies and the provision of public services at the local level, as, for example, (1) studies of the impact of the property tax on location decisions, land use, and housing maintenance, and (2) the costs and benefits of new types of user charges;

• the effects of legal controls, as, for example, (1) the nature and outcomes of the bargaining process between city developers and regulating agencies, and (2) the potential benefits of new legal definitions of ownership; and

• the social and institutional setting of housing programs, as, for example, (1) alternative measures of housing quality, and (2) functional criteria for density controls.

With respect to the successful implementation of available technology and to provide a base for further technological program development as social requirements are identified, the Committee on Urban Technology recommends to the Department of Housing and Urban Development that

• a series of carefully chosen large-scale experiments should be undertaken to explore the significant applications and implications of balanced systems for community development; the Department is urged to take the leadership in continued exploration of opportunities for further developments in industrialized housing production;

• the potential opportunities of the community service center concept for the organization and distribution of discretionary services should be studied and evaluated. An early stage of the research should explore appropriate layouts and combinations of facilities;

• the feasibility and usefulness of sophisticated systems for nondiscretionary services should be evaluated in full-scale field experiments in several communities and in several variations. Such experiments should work to evaluate the desirability and economics of combined service tunnels for utilities, such as water, energy, communication, chilled water for air conditioning, and waste disposal;

• consideration of improvement of rail-guided and independently controlled vehicles for use in urban areas and of short-haul aircraft technology should be a part of urban transportation planning; in Departmental programs associated with the planning of expensive long-lived public facilities systems, allowance should be made for further application of forecasted technology to avoid obsolescence;

• efforts should be made to encourage further development needed for adapting the performance criteria concept as a possible alternative to design-specification-type building code; and research for low-cost housing should seek means to reduce all cost elements, especially those outside of construction, and should consider the mixed utilization of new construction, refurbishing, upgrading, and relocation.

COMMITTEE ON SOCIAL AND BEHAVIORAL URBAN RESEARCH

RAYMOND A. BAUER, *Chairman;* Harvard University
EDMUND N. BACON, Philadelphia City Planning Commission
BRIAN J. L. BERRY, University of Chicago
HARVEY E. BRAZER, University of Michigan
LINCOLN H. DAY, Yale University
NATHAN GLAZER, University of California, Berkeley
AMOS H. HAWLEY, University of North Carolina
EVERETT S. LEE, University of Massachusetts
NORTON E. LONG, Brandeis University
DANIEL R. MANDELKER, Washington University
WILLIAM R. MASON, The Irvine Company
ALVIN M. WEINBERG and JAMES C. BRESEE (alternate), Oak Ridge National Laboratory
ABEL WOLMAN, The Johns Hopkins University
PAUL N. YLVISAKER, Department of Community Affairs, State of New Jersey

ALEXANDER L. CLARK, *Executive Secretary;* Division of Behavioral Sciences

COMMITTEE ON URBAN TECHNOLOGY

JAMES F. YOUNG, *Chairman;* General Electric Company
GENE M. AMDAHL, International Business Machines
GORDON S. BROWN, Massachusetts Institute of Technology
ANGUS CAMPBELL, University of Michigan
JOHN H. DESSAUER, Xerox Corporation
ROBERT H. DIETZ, University of Washington
LAWRENCE R. HAFSTAD, General Motors Corporation
T. Y. LINN, University of California, Berkeley
ROBINSON NEWCOMB, Consulting Economist
JOSEPH H. NEWMAN, Tishman Realty & Construction Company, Inc.

STUART M. CHARLESWORTH, *Executive Secretary;* Division of Engineering
JAMES R. KINGHAM, *Staff Editor*

DATE DUE

			PRINTED IN U.S.A.